THIS ANNUAL BELONGS TO:

Name: Jake

Address: 146 sairmeera
aVehne

EDITORIAL Editor: David Leach • **Designer**: Donna Askem • Thanks to Becky Lord

TITAN COMICS Senior Comics Editor: Martin Eden • **Production Supervisors** Jackie Flock, Maria Pearson • **Production Assistant** Peter James • **Art Director** Oz Browne
Studio Manager Selina Juneja • **Circulation Manager** Steve Tothill • **Marketing Manager** Ricky Claydon • **Marketing Assistant** Rebecca Lonergan • **Advertising Manager**
Michelle Fairlamb • **Publishing Manager** Darryl Tothill • **Publishing Director** Chris Teather • **Operations Director** Leigh Baulch • **Executive Director** Vivian Cheung
Publisher Nick Landau

ADVENTURE TIME Annual 2016

ISBN: 9781782765974

A CIP catalogue record for this title is available from the British Library.

Printed in Italy.

This edition first published: August 2015

CONTENTS

Greetings fellow adventurers, see how many times you can find me hiding out in this annual! Turn to page 68 for the answer.

AAAAAHHHHHHHHHHHHHHHHHHH! YOU GUYS, AAAAHHHHHHHHH!!

IT'S THE WORST THING TO EVER HAPPEN

TO ANYONE

IN THE ENTIRE HISTORY OF TIME!!

KLK

What?

What??

WHAT???

SOMEBODY...

STOLE...

MY...

STAAAR!!

It's a JEWEL, you guys! And somebody STOLE IT, probably to buy some stupid garbage like GROSS WHEAT or CORN!!

Stay right there, LSP. We're on our way down.

Yeah!!

Wait, why are we talking smack about corn??

Because it's gross AND nasty AND gross-nasty? But that's not important right now! MY STAR IS STOLEN!!

Is someone throwing shade on corn??

Lumpy Space Princess says she doesn't like delicious corn!

Oh my GLOB, everyone stop talking about corn and come outside and help me!!

Alright alright, calm DOWN, LSP.

Your heroes are on their way, m'lady!!

Hey, have you ever tried it with a nice slab of butter on top? DELICIOUS.

CORN'S GROSS AND YOU ACTUALLY JUST LIKE BUTTER, ICE KING!!

OPEN YOUR EYES!

Alright, LSP, tell us everything you know about what happened.

Yeah! The more we know, the better we'll be able to track down the thief!

Nice try, friendos! But I know the first rule of investigating crimes:

Don't give away any prime information...TO YOUR PRIME SUSPECTS.

Suspects? What?

That's right, Marceline! Y'ALL ARE TIED AS MY #1 SUSPECTS!!

DRAAAAMA BOMB!

LSP, we wouldn't steal your star! We peeps are WAY good-aligned!

Yeah!

I mean... generally.

Save it, chumps! I know it was one of you, and I hope y'all have some RAD ALIBIS because y'all are getting QUESTIONED on the ASAP!!

Come on, LSP. I don't even want your star. Besides, my alibi is AIR-TIGHT.

Yeah! And MY alibi is air-tighter, LSP!!

MY ALIBI IS I WAS PARTYING

Alright, "BMO", if that **IS** your real name--

It is! Yaaaay!

Why don't you tell me **EXACTLY** where you were during the night of the theft?

Okay! I love telling stories!!

BMO's ALIBI

"It was a dark and stormy night. The kind of night that made you think someone might be out there doing a crime in it somewhere."

What's this? An invitation??

Princess Bubblegum cordially invites BMO to attend her SECRET PRINCESS MEETING after which Light Refreshments will be served. TELL NO ONE

"The invitation seemed legit, and word was the old lady had been trying to get her claws into me for a while. I decided to humor her."

Yaaay! A party!!

Introduction

This is the sequel to *Pits: A Pictorial History of Mining in Barnsley*, published in June, 1987. To avoid repetition, we have had to adopt an unusual format for this book. Basically it has been split into two: the first part concentrates on the growth of mining in the nineteenth century and relies on words, photographs and illustrations. Much of the material has not been published for more than a hundred years, particularly the chapter dealing with women and children underground. In the recent past, some of the evidence given to the commissioners would not have been published on grounds of bad taste but in a more enlightened era the quotes seem quite tame.

The second half of the book concentrates on the twentieth century and relies more on photographs and illustrations than words. The history of mining has not been adequately photographed and we have had to draw on outside sources to add some character and atmosphere to the book.

Barnsley Library's Local Studies Department has a wealth of material and we were fortunate to have the opportunity to read four first-class accounts dealing with pit life in the last century: a book written by Edward Rymer, a former miner, in the 1890s; a diary written by Joseph Knowles, of Hemingfield; and books on the Clarkes of Silkstone and the Fitzwilliams of Wentworth Woodhouse, which have been invaluable. Mr. A. O. Elmhirst also deserves a 'thank you' for the documents relating to his family.

For a hundred years mining has played a dominant part in the life of Barnsley. With the disastrous 1984/85 miners' strike, and the subsequent pit closure programme, the days of mining appear to be numbered. The book is dedicated to the men who worked in the mines and to the Yorkshire Mining Museum at the former Caphouse Colliery.

Below: The Yorkshire Mining Museum, Caphouse Colliery. As part of the musuem tour, visitors have the opportunity to travel 140 metres down the shaft to the New Hards Seam. The guided underground tour demonstrates the conditions and methods of mining from the early 1800s to the present day. The main exhibit is Caphouse Colliery itself. Its core is the wooden headstock and the stone engine house, both erected in 1876. The headstock is probably the last one made of wood that survives in Yorkshire, while in the engine house is the original Davy Bros. twin cylinder steam winding engine. It was used regularly until 1974 and, occasionally, until 1981. However the oldest feature of the pit is not a building but the main shaft, which appeared on a map completed in 1795.

There are no restrictions on age, although it is not possible to take very young children down the pit. Parties are admitted at a reduced rate and must be booked in advance.

Right: Illustration of the Lundhill
Colliery explosion, 1857.
John Goodchild Collection

EARLY MINING

Chapter 1
The growth of the pits

In the early Victorian era someone described Widnes as *"a new, crude, growing town."* The same words could have applied to Barnsley in the 1850s and 1860s, a jumble of smoking slopes and hollows sandwiched between the wind-swept moors and what was described as the rich and beautiful countryside at Wombwell and Worsbrough.

Coal was first outcropped and then mined on the outskirts of Barnsley, in villages like Silkstone, but the land was merely scratched. As the nation underwent one of its spasmodic convulsions, changing from a society based on agriculture to one based on industry, the richer, deeper seams were exploited in Barnsley, and later in the Dearne Valley. The area changed beyond recognition, absorbing all the clutter and paraphernalia of mining: spoil heaps, back-to-back houses, canals, railways and subsidence (in the early 1860s the Guardians of the Poor were complaining that subsidence from Mr. Greaves's pit was damaging the workhouse). Mining also saved Barnsley from economic collapse as the linen industry contracted.

After 1850, when the first train arrived in Barnsley, shafts were sunk all over the town: some resembled modern mines, others were glorified holes in the ground. The mine owners came from a wide variety of backgrounds and included aristocrats, landowners, the landed gentry, hard-nosed businessmen, a bank clerk, iron manufacturers, men who had made money in the linen industry, a railway engineer and men who were not much better off than their hewers.

The aristocrats were the Fitzwilliams, of Wentworth Woodhouse, who had the largest estate in South Yorkshire. Unlike most big landowners, who were content to lease the mineral rights to groups of men, the Fitzwilliams went into mining in a big way, in Elsecar, Jump and Hemingfield. A pit was working at Elsecar before 1750. Most of the owners were spurred on by need and greed but the Fitzwilliams set up a miniature welfare state, providing cheap and decent housing; home coal; schools and medical facilities. Many technical innovations were intro-

duced at their well managed pits, including the Newcomen steam engine, which began pumping water at a 1,000 gallons a minute from 1795, and which can still be seen near the site of the former Elsecar Main Colliery.

Families like the Elmhirsts found themselves sitting on valuable seams of coal. In 1718 Worsbrough old town account books noted the payment of 17s. to Mr. Elmhirst for four loads of coal. In April, 1765, John Tattershall was buried in Worsbrough church yard, *"a collier killed in Mr. Elmhirst's pit."* Mining was still primitive. Coal was brought to the surface and then had to remain there until horses and carts arrived. The demand for coal was growing, overwhelming the primitive transport available, and landowners,

Below: The Newcomen steam engine (left of photograph) one of the Fitzwilliam's innovations still stands near the site of the former Elsecar Main Colliery.
Photo: British Coal (1950s)

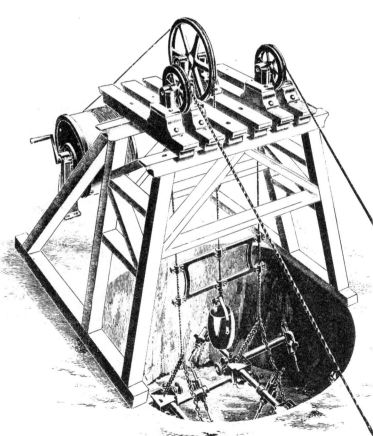

PATENT SIGNAL BELLS,

For Collieries, Railways, &c.,

MANUFACTURED BY

M. LOWRANCE & SON,

PEEL SQUARE, BARNSLEY.

TESTIMONIALS.

From Strafford Collieries, near Barnsley.

Messrs. M. Lowrance & Sons, Barnsley.

DEAR SIRS,
In reply to yours of the 3rd instant, we have much pleasure in stating that we have had the patent Signal Bells as supplied by you in constant use here for about three years, and that they give general satisfaction, and are undoubtedly the best that have been brought under our notice.

Yours truly,
Pro The Strafford Coal Co., Limited, C. F. SEWARD.

From Wharncliffe Silkstone Collieries, near Sheffield.

To M. Lowrance & Son, Barnsley.

GENTLEMEN.
In reply to your enquiry of the 3rd instant, we have to state that we have 16 of the Patent Signal Bells in use, and that we have found them the least liable to get out of repair of any we have had.

Yours truly,
Pro Wharncliffe Silkstone Coal Co., HORACE WALKER.

From Thornhill Collieries, near Dewsbury.

DEAR SIRS,
In reply to your enquiry as to the efficiency of the Patent Signal Bells I beg to say that we have about a dozen of them at work at these Collieries, and find them infinitely superior to anything we have had before. We have used them for, I think fully three years, and have never had one out of order.

Mr. John Lowrance.

Yours truly,
W. P. MADDISON.

Chapter 2
Women and children

When colliers walked through the streets of Barnsley in the 1830s and early 1840s, all grime and muscle, wearing trousers and shirts and thick wooden clogs, the onlookers could not distinguish to which sex they belonged. For years women had worked at the older pits at Silkstone where some were expected to hew coal like men; now, with the coalfield moving eastwards, they were becoming a familiar sight on Barnsley streets.

With perseverance, the local population believed they could tolerate the uncouth and swarthy male miners but the middle classes, both in Barnsley and beyond, could not come to terms with pit women. According to one Victorian writer, women were supposed to be angels, not animals like men. So pit women were seen as either innocent victims of a brutal industrial system, *"sacrificed to the shameless indecencies of working underground,"* according to the Children's Employment Commission, or as liberated creatures endowed with too many unseemly male characteristics, incapable of performing the duties imposed on women in Victorian society. The reformist and missionary zeal of the nation's middle classes was just waiting to be released.

The women and children aged up to 17 or 18, all known as hurriers, were used to take coal from the coal face to the shaft, sometimes harnessed like dogs to a cart, crawling on their hands and feet, pulling heavy tubs behind them. The coal hewers, self employed men, hired and paid them; the proprietors were responsible for discipline. In 1840 the Children's Employment Commission set up to investigate the mental and moral conditions of the mines, particularly in respect of children, revealed that there were 22 adult women for every 1,000 men in the pits; 36 girls aged between 13 and 18 for every 246 boys of the same age; and 41 girls under 13 for every 246 boys of that age group. The commission, some people believed, had been set up too late to deal with the problem of women, the use of them in the mines having started to decline in the late eighteenth century when proprietors found horses were cheaper and stronger in the newly developed thicker seams. Some proprietors, like the Fitzwilliams, who owned pits in Elsecar, Jump and Hemingfield, did not permit women to work underground in the nineteenth century. But the sub-commissioner said *"oppressively hard work was performed by young females at other Barnsley pits,"* and added: *"were they galley-slaves their work would not be so oppressive."* Elizabeth Day, aged 17, who worked at Hopwood's Pit, Barnsley, told the sub-commissioner she had to push or pull corves (carriages for carrying coal) up slopes, adding:

"I have been nearly nine years at the pit. I trapped two years and have been a hurrier ever since. When I riddle, I hold the riddle, shake it to remove the slack and then throw the rest into the corve. I work naked to the waist."

Ann Eggley, aged 18, who worked at Thorp's Pit, said:

"The work is very hard. The sweat runs all over sometimes. Father said last night it was both a shame and a disgrace for girls to work as we do but there was nowt else for us to do. Sometimes we get home at night and we haven't the power to wash ourselves. We work twelve hours per day. We wear trousers and great big boots, clinkered and nailed. The girls at our pit do not work naked to the waist."

Her father, James Eggley, aged 45, said he had six girls, and a boy who was not old enough to work down the pit and the girls had to go underground to earn money.

Right: Women were treated like galley-slaves — sometimes they were harnessed like dogs to a cart, *"crawling on their hands and feet, pulling heavy tubs behind them."*

According to the sub-commissioner, labour was distributed indifferently among both sexes except that it was rare for both men and women to hew coal. Men worked naked, assisted by females of all ages, from girls of six to women of 21, with females naked to the waist. He wrote:

"One of the most disgusting sights I have ever seen was of young females, dressed like boys in trousers, crawling on all fours, with belts round the waists and chains passing between their legs, in pits near Holmfirth and New Mill. Two of the girls had worn large holes in their trousers and any sight more disgusting or revolting can scarcely be imagined than these girls at work — no brothel can beat it."

On descending Hopwood's Pit, Barnsley, he found sitting round a fire a group of girls, some of whom were at the age of puberty, the girls as well as the boys naked to the waist.

"Their sex was only recognisable by their breasts. I had some difficulty on occasions pointing out which were girls and which were boys and that caused a great deal of laughter and joking."

Edward Newman, a solicitor of Barnsley, displayed all the double standards of the Victorian age. He abhorred the sight of half-naked girls — but he could not resist peering into their homes when they were washing.

"There are a great many girls at Silkstone who work in the pits and I have seen them washing much below the waists as I passed their doors and as they are doing that they will be chatting and talking with any man who happens to be there. Men, young and old, are washing in the same place at the same time. They dress so well after their work, and on Sundays, that it is impossible to recognise them. They wear ear-rings even whilst at work and I have seen them with ear-rings nearly two inches long. There is a great deal of loud talk and slang between the lads and girls as they pass along the streets from work and I believe they would behave more decorously were it not for the dress and disguise it affords. I have never heard similar language pass between people respectably dressed in Barnsley."

Matthew Lindley, who worked at a Barnsley pit owned by Day and Twibell:

"I wish the Government would expel all girls and women from the mines. I can give proof that they are immoral, and I am certain that the girls are worse than the men as far as morals are concerned, and use far more indecent language. It unbecomes them in every way; there is not one out of ten of them who knows how to cut out a shirt, or make one, and they learn neither to sew nor knit. I have known of a case myself where a married miner and a girl who hurried for him had sexual intercourse on the bank where they worked."

George Armitage, a 35 years old Hoyland teacher, and a collier until he was 22, said no doubt debauchery took place and added:

"I think it is scarcely possible for girls to remain modest, regularly mixing with such company and hearing such language."

A Silkstone woman:

"I am informed that in some pits scenes pass which are as bad as in a house of ill fame; this I have been told by young men who work in the pits."

Michael Thomas Sadler, a surgeon of Barnsley:

"The female character is destroyed by the mines. I see the greatest differences in the homes of those colliers whose wives do not go down the mines in cleanliness and good management. The pit women neither discharge their duties as wives nor mothers."

Below: Women worked underground until the early 1840s. At Silkstone they were expected to dig coal like men but at most pits they were used to pull or push coal tubs. The withdrawal of women underground led to protests from some coal owners, who thought a labour shortage would hit the mines, and from some miners who wanted their daughters to have highly paid jobs.
Published by courtesy of the Fellows of Trinity College, Cambridge.

23

Right: Post cards of Lancashire women were popular during the nineteenth century. The middle classes, who bought the post cards, were fascinated by the sight of women dressed in men's clothes. Tourists often turned up at the pits to peep at the women and management at one mine had to ban the curious onlookers because they were a nuisance.

Published by courtesy of the Wigan Record Office.

24

John Thorneley, described as a JP in the county of York:

"The young of both sexes work in a half naked state and passions are excited."

John Cawthra, a collier at Messrs. Wilson's Pit, Barnsley:

"I do not think it is a good system to bring girls down the pit; they get bold and it tends to make the girls have bastards."

Matthew Fountain, underground steward at Darton Pit, owned by Thomas Wilson, believed that sexual intercourse took place and added:

"Girls work as well as boys but they can't make a shirt."

Joseph Ellison, of Leeds, said he knew of the case of a girl, employed as a hurrier by her father-in-law, who refused to go down the mines again because he tried to ravish her.

A vivid account of similar working lives underground in French pits is contained in Emile Zola's book, *Germinal*, in which he refers to girls who could move tubs as well as grown women, *"in spite of doll-like arms,"* and of young women who *"could take on two pit boys together."* He wrote:

"... but the voice of the receiver shouted up orders to dispatch — doubtless some deputy was on the prowl down there. Movement began again on all nine levels, and nothing could be heard but the regular calls of the boys and snorting of the haulage girls as they reached the incline, all steaming like overloaded mares. It was at times like this that one of the waves of bestiality ran through the mine, the sudden lust of the male that came over the miner when they met one of the girls."

All kinds of arguments were put forward to try to stop the withdrawal of women from the pits. Coal proprietor John Hopwood said there could be labour shortages in Barnsley. But the loudest protest came from some colliers who were more concerned about finding jobs for their daughters than morals. However, there were exceptions. In the late 1830s a large gathering of miners in Barnsley passed a resolution urging the withdrawal on the grounds that the use of women was a shameful practice.

Above: Working on the pit surface, in all kinds of weather, may not seem to be the ideal job for anyone; but there is some evidence to suggest that the women pit workers enjoyed their work, or perhaps they needed the money. When there was a move to ban women working at the pit head, the Wigan women organised a protest demonstration in London.
Published by courtesy of the Fellows of Trinity College, Cambridge.

Children

Members of the commission were told that children of three and four were frequently taken down the mines. One collier said he took his child of three underground with him and it was made to follow him into the workings. The child held a candle and when exhausted with fatigue was cradled on the coals until the collier returned home at night.

Edward Ellis, surgeon, of Silkstone, said:

"I have 25 professional years' service among colliers. The children round here go down the pits at five."

The Reverend Richard Morton, a curate at Dodworth, said parents got their children into the pits as soon as they could do the task. Matthew Lindley, collier:

"Children are sometimes brought to the pit at the age of six, and are taken out of their beds between 4 and 5 a.m. throughout the year."

John Twibell, coal owner:

"My opinion is that children should not be employed until the age of ten. We intend to direct our attention to this point with a view to it being made a rule of the pit. I am aware that some children are working as young as seven in some pits. I look on this as objectionable, both on the grounds of health and education."

The youngest children worked as trappers. They sat in a little hole with a length of string attached to an air-door; when they heard the approaching corves they pulled the string and opened the door. They worked twelve hours per day, sitting in the dark, often on a damp floor and exposed to draughts. The sub-commissioner wrote:

"It is a most painful thing to contemplate the

ered in France. It wasn't until the 1880s that science and experience had reduced the likelihood of explosions. Experiments were also beginning to show that explosions of coal dust and the air were possible in the absence of fire-damp (the term given to inflammable gas or mixture of gases). On the other hand, the nineteenth century did not see any improvement in the number of deaths due to roof falls. In the early twentieth century roof falls were the most common cause of death, accounting for sixty per cent of fatalities as against only ten per cent on average from explosions.

The perils of early mining were chronicled by local newspapers. In the 1850s and 1860s accidents were weekly occurrences. Both men and management were indifferent to risks: wage packets and profits depended on how much coal was brought up the shafts. Every week the lists of accidents appeared in the newspapers. During a week in 1861, for example, Edward Frost was killed at Low Valley pit; John Tomlinson, of Baker Street, was crushed at Oaks Colliery; George Clapham, of Market Street, severely injured at Old Mill Colliery; and a Mr. Spink, of Ardsley, injured in a roof fall at Darfield Main. There were accidents at East Gawber, Mount Osborne and Agnes Main Collieries during a week in June, 1863. At the latter pit Messrs. Simmons and Edge, of Barebones, were severely burnt while using candles. Not all the accidents were underground. Surface tramways could be a menace. In October, 1863, a 55 years old man and seven years old boy were on a cart crossing a tramway belonging to Vizard's Pit, Jump, when a convoy of coal wagons travelling down an incline en route to the canal at Elsecar ran into the

cart. The man's horse was killed on the spot and the man and boy died a few minutes later. These news items were often relegated to the depths of the newspaper columns, indicating that in the view of the Editor — and therefore the public — they were frequent and minor incidents.

The headlines were captured by the disasters. The explosion at Lundhill Colliery, Wombwell, was one of the worst. Nearly 200 were killed there in 1857; yet on the Sunday following the disaster on the Thursday the mood at the pit head was one of laughter. A London reporter wrote:

"The level ground and the steep slope between Wombwell and the colliery was crowded with people,

Above: The late Joe Short, a Wombwell photographer, took this photograph of a Mr. and Mrs. Rhodes in Lundhill Row in the 1920s. It is believed the couple could recall the Lundhill disaster in 1857.

Left: Another example of a dramatic mining disaster in a Victorian newspaper.

NOTABLE COLLIERY EXPLOSIONS AND MINING DISASTERS IN YORKSHIRE SINCE 1672.

AT the request of a number of our patrons we have reproduced the local colliery explosions in a somewhat more extended form, and have added short notices of the most serious disasters which have unfortunately occurred from time to time in connection with the working of coal in the county, which can be traced back to early in the fourteenth century. Unfortunately the Barnsley district, owing to the fiery nature of some of the seams, has at times been the scene of some very sad disasters. The Rev. W. Thorp, B.A., vicar of Misson, Notts., in a pamphlet on "The Causes of the Explosions in the Barnsley, or Thick Coal of Yorkshire," states that from 1841 to 1857, when his pamphlet was printed, 450 persons perished by fire damp in the pits in the Barnsley districts alone. There were also at one time many serious outbursts of gas, chiefly in the Silkstone seam, of which little is now heard, and the district for some time has been happily free from serious disaster. The most serious mishaps are as under :—

1672, July 11. Colliery explosion at Barnsley, when a miner named James Townend was killed.

1755, May 2nd. Explosion at Mr. Boden's pit, Genne Lane, when John Tasker, Thos. Horsforth, and Geo. Burdett were killed by fire damp. The register of Worsbro' Church contains an entry of these men's deaths.

1797. Explosion at a Rothwell Haigh colliery, thirteen men and boys killed. Amongst those who perished was a father and four sons.

1803. A terrific explosion occurred at the Barmby Furnace Colliery, which was sunk by the Low Moor Company about 1802, on land leased from the late Walter Spencer Stanhope, of Cannon Hall, between 28 to 30 persons lost their lives.

1805, August 19th. Explosion at Barmby Furnace Colliery, which resulted in the death of seven men, including John and Mark Teasdale (brothers), who had come to sink the shafts from the north of England. The explosion was caused by the gas coming in contact with the naked light.

1809, June 30. A lamentable accident occurred at Messrs. Lee, Watson, and Company's colliery, East Ardsley, near Wakefield, owing to an immense body of water rushing out of some old workings. Ten men and boys were drowned, four were rescued after being entombed three days and nights.

1821, May 23. Serious accident at Norcroft Colliery in the township of Cawthorne. Eleven persons were ascending the shaft when the chain broke and they were precipitated to the bottom, a depth of nearly sixty yards. Seven were killed and two died afterwards. Nine lives lost.

1822, July. Five men were killed by fire damp in a colliery near Sheffield.

1825, January 12. Explosion at the Garforth Colliery, Middleton, near Leeds. Twenty-five men and boys perished.

In affectionate Remembrance of
THE LATE GEORGE DAWSON,
Of West-Melton, aged 26 years,
Who lost his life by the awful Explosion at Lund-Hill Colliery, February 19th, 1857,
And was recovered from the Pit June 22nd, and interred at Christ Church, West-Melton, June 26th, 1857.

At five o'clock he left his horse,
Upon that fatal morn ;
And little thought upon the road,
He never must return.

He reach'd the pit and did descend,
To labour underground ;
While danger did each step attend,
And darkness all around.

We hope the Lord received his soul,
With Him always to dwell ;
The sufferings he did undergo,
No mortal tongue can tell.

IN LIFE RESPECTED AND IN DEATH REGRETED.

and when the decision to close the pit was made known it staggered the hopeful and appalled to silence those who had dared to hope that yet many human beings might be got up alive. This measure showed that hope was abandoned. It was felt that no further search could be made while the fire raged, and that no-one could get through the fire to the shaft.

"As is not unusual on such occasions the behaviour of the masses was not exemplary. Every train today (there was a platform at Lundhill on the South Yorkshire Coal Railway) has brought a large number of excursionists who by their conduct seemed bound to a fair or country fete rather than the scene of a frightful calamity. Each road leading to the colliery was covered with throngs of people dotting the highway for miles in every direction. The immediate neighbourhood of the colliery could only be compared with Greenwich Hill on a summer day. At two o'clock

this afternoon there were from 10,000 to 15,000 persons at the spot, and few indeed were there who appeared to realise that they were standing over the bodies of nearly 200 human beings hurled without a moment's notice to eternity. In the dense crowd the loud laugh and jest were heard incessantly. The larger part of the crowd were neighbouring pit men and their wives. It is difficult to understand the callousness of their behaviour with those of whose voices were raised occasionally in hymns."

After the disaster, William Hopton, of Carlton, wrote in *Conversations on Mines*:

"The ventilation of this pit was so bad that I took it on myself to publish a plan of the pit and expose the system. This caused a discussion which continued for sixteen weeks in the mining newspapers. Afterwards I received a letter from Nicholas Wood, president of the Mining Institute, requesting me to become a member and offering to pay my yearly contributions. I declined the offer with thanks, fearing that I should be asked to attend meetings at Newcastle, which my means would not allow."

Following publication of his article, he was hounded from place to place and his family reduced to poverty, although he later settled in Lancashire and achieved distinction in the mining world.

Arriving by train at Lundhill, two years after the disaster, a journalist wrote:

"Like the ruins of a battle-field, the signs of such a catastrophe are soon cleared away, but the widows

Notable Colliery Explosions and Disasters.

1833, May 30. Explosion at Lindley Top Colliery, near Huddersfield. Five killed.

1836, August 22. Explosion at Worsbro' Park Colliery, near Barnsley. Three killed.

1836, December 13. Explosion at the Bog Pit, near Wakefield. Thirteen men and six boys were badly burnt, and several died from the effects of the injuries.

1838, February 16. Explosion at the Robin Hood Colliery, near Wakefield, belonging to Messrs. Charlesworth. Several killed.

1838, July 4. During a terrific storm of thunder and hail the valley on the south-west side of Dodworth was inundated. The water rose to such a height that it reached a coal pit on the hill side, belonging to the late Mr. R. C. Clarke, of Noblethorpe, called the Moor Side pit, and twenty-six persons were drowned, eleven of them being females. Fourteen of the largest escaped by getting into the old slit ends. Those drowned were from seven to seventeen years of age. A monument was erected in Silkstone church yard as a reminder of the sad event.

1839, May 29. Three brothers named Jaggar and another miner named John Robinson were killed at Worsbro' Park pit by an accident.

1841, November 21. About six o'clock this morning an explosion occurred at Mount Osborne Colliery, Barnsley, when four miners and eleven hurriers were killed, and a man named Edward Walton lost his life whilst descending the shaft in a corf.

1842, February 21st. Explosion at Hopwood's Colliery, Cockerham Road, Barnsley. Killed : Fanny Day, fifteen years ; Ann Mallinson, sixteen years ; Martha Mallinson, fifteen years. Mallinsons' father had died three weeks before the explosion. There were two explosions.

1843, April 14. Explosion at Darley Main Colliery, Worsbro' Dale, one life lost.

1845, June 11. Explosion at the Oaks Colliery, which then belonged to Messrs. Firth, Barber, & Co. Three killed.

1847, January 29. Six men lost their lives at Darley Main Colliery by choke damp from the ignition of gas in blasting coal with gunpowder. Five of the men were married and one single. They were interred in one grave in Worsbro' Churchyard.

1847, March 5. Explosion at the Oaks Colliery, near Barnsley. Ninety-seven men were in the workings, 73 of whom were killed. The explosion, which was a terrific one, originated in an old break or abandoned working. Though the shafts were 283 yards deep, the explosion was so violent that the noise of it was heard at a distance of several miles. The verdict of the jury was "Accidental Death," but the jury were of opinion that efficient regulations were not enforced in the district to prevent the use of naked lights in those parts of the mine in which inflammable gas was known to exist. Forty-six of the victims were interred in the St. Mary's Burial Ground, Barnsley ; thirteen at Ardsley ; and the rest in different parishes. Twenty-five of those killed were married men and left twenty-three widows and sixty-three children. Only five of the married victims were over forty, and only two of the forty-eight single men were thirty years of age. A subscription was set on foot which raised about £1,000.

1847, May 15. Explosion at Beeston Main Colliery, near Leeds. Nine lives lost.

1847, August. Another explosion at Darley Main Colliery. Two killed.

and orphans still remain. They received the train with wonder, smiles and shouts — a dense crowd of sunburnt women and children, whose clean caps and aprons look doubly and deceptively clean, brought out, as they are, by the background of black ashes, smoke and coal-dust. I took my place in the cage in front of a pale-faced gentleman, who looked as if the signal for letting us down was the signal of death to him, and he was perfectly aware of it. Not a sound was heard, nor the whisper of a voice, as we glided down the perpendicular passage, except at one point, about 15 yards from the mouth of the shaft. The top of the pit being on a raised platform, the chimney of the shaft is exposed above the ground for a certain length, and a window is made on each side, near the point where the chimney disappears beneath the surface of the earth, to give a little light during some portion of the descent. At each of these windows, leaning on the ledges and grinning through the grating, were a crowd of brown-faced orphans, and as the cage passed their faces on its rapid road to the black passages where their fathers had perished, they greeted it with a combined, re-echoing yell of childish joy. Not only were the traces of the explosion removed from the neighbourhood, but time has also removed them from these children's hearts.

"... Another step was to get hold of a talkative boy, who was full of stories about the explosion, and to follow him to a forbidden part of the pit, called the waste workings, and see the outstretched mark of a

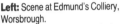

Left: Scene at Edmund's Colliery, Worsbrough.
Published by permission of The Illustrated London News.

THE EXPLOSION ON WEDNESDAY WEEK AT EDMUND'S MAIN COLLIERY, BARNSLEY.—SEE NEXT PAGE.

39

Right: The Swaithe Main disaster memorial at St. Thomas's Church, Worsbrough.

were allowed to continue. The feeling that there was no danger and that no-one need to be worried was the prime cause of the lamentable loss of life. Many men working some distance from the fire were not warned. The explosion occurred at eleven o'clock. The gas which followed the explosion spread through the pit and survivors told how they stumbled over the dead and dying, and there was confusion and panic at the main shaft because the cages were packed. A survivor, a George Stubbs, said he fell over ten or twelve bodies of dead and dying men and he had to stuff his cotton cap into his mouth to keep out the gas."

The passages were full of gas and there was a

Notable Colliery Explosions and Disasters.

1860, February 15. Explosion at the Higham Colliery, the property of Messrs. Charlesworth, thirteen being killed. Their names were David Jagger, married, aged 78; David Jagger, 14, grandson of the former; George Cawthorne, 35, married, three children; George Summers, 12; Hy. Richardson, 12, of Cawthorne; John Wilson, 40, married, two children; Jos. Wilson, 14, son of the former; Jos. Clarke, 23, single; John Whitehead, 30, married, three children; Henry Brown, 12, of Higham; William Depledge, 26. Henry Wilson and John Wilson, father and son, and John Crossley, of Higham, were got out alive but died afterwards.

1860, March 8. Richard Padgett, 52, and Thos. Carr, deputy stewards, killed at Strafford Main Colliery whilst removing brattices. Each left a widow and nine children.

1860, April 12. Charles Meggitt, of Sheffield, killed by a fire at the Masbro Moor pit. The steward, John Sissions was censured by the jury.

1861, January 1. Two men were killed at the Brown Moor Colliery, near Seacroft, Leeds, by the breaking of the crank of the engine, as they were being lowered down the shaft.

1861, June 26. Explosion at Old Mill Colliery caused by sudden fall of roof. A young man named Rolling lost his life by choke damp and 28 persons were burnt by the explosion.

1861, July 27. Explosion at East Gawber Hall Colliery, two lives lost.

1862, April 4. Explosion at Sowhill Colliery, near Chapeltown. Six men killed. Verdict of jury, "Accidental death," with an expression of opinion that it was unsafe to work with naked lights near a roof.

1862, April 4, October 8, 1863, February 15, 1870, July 4, 1870, August 29. Five alarming outbursts of gas occurred on the dates named in the Silkstone seam at Messrs. Newton, Chambers, & Co.'s, Thorncliffe Collieries. The first of the two fatal explosions occurred when naked lights were used and the second at the furnaces. At the time the first explosion occurred the firm had worked the collieries for 68 years, and during that period outbursts of gas were unknown.

1862, December 8. Explosion at Edmunds Main, Worsbro' Dale, belonging to Messrs. Mitchell & Co. 260 persons were in the mine, and 59 men perished. The mine was flooded, and some bodies were not recovered until the 15th of June. At the inquest the verdict returned was "Accidental Death." The jury expressed the unanimous opinion that the cause of the explosion was owing to incautious and unsafe working of the dip board of the colliery. The owners were proceeded against by the Miners' National Union on behalf of 34 widows, to obtain compensation under Lord Campbell's Act, and ultimately legal proceedings were withdrawn, upon the owners, whilst denying their legal liability, paying £1,550.

1863, November 30. Six miners killed at Thrybergh Hall Colliery, near Swinton, by falling down the shaft, a depth of 150 yards, caused by the overturning of the "chair" in which the deceased were descending the shaft.

1865, October 23. Explosion at one of the collieries, owned by Messrs. Unwin and Shaw, Brightside, near Sheffield, caused by the use of naked lights. One man was killed and three others seriously injured.

1866, November 29. Three men, named Frank Howden, 36; Jos. Ogden, 56; and Benjamin Goodcliffe, were killed by the breaking of a rope whilst descending the shaft of the Wharncliffe Silkstone Colliery, Pilley.

man's form impressed on the roof. This man must have floated up after the pit was flooded with water to put out the fire, and the water was charged with lime to prevent decomposition in the one hundred and ninety bodies; and he left a white seal of himself to be the talk of miners for many years."

Five years later, on December 8, 1862, disaster struck at a colliery three miles from Lundhill. Fiftynine miners were killed in an explosion at Edmund's Main Colliery, Worsbrough Dale.

The colliery, owned by Mitchell, Bartholomew and Tyas, was situated near the South Yorkshire Coal line and the Dearne and Dove canal. The workings at the nine years old mine had been extended 1,800 yards to form a connection with the new Swaithe shaft. More than 300 men and boys worked in the nine feet thick seams, and most of them were working round the clock, the reckless pursuit of coal and bonus payments being one of the contributory factors in the explosion.

The explosion was caused by a fire in the workings near the Swaithe shaft. Gas was ignited and a seam of coal caught fire. A reporter for the *Barnsley Chronicle* wrote:

"There was an incessant emission of gas and it certainly seems peculiar why blasting operations

danger of another explosion — there were fears the fire was still burning, so the owners made a decision to flood the pit. A ditch was dug from a stream near the canal, a decision which angered young miners because they thought they should make another rescue bid. The crowd at the pit head was on the verge of rioting and a stone was thrown through an office window. When the sluice was opened, and water poured down the mine, the cupola spewed out smoke, revealing that the fire was still burning.

The disaster caused a sensation. The December 20th issue of the *Chronicle* disclosed that thousands of spectators arrived on the previous Sunday from all parts of the country. At 8 a.m. a crowd surged up Sheffield Road and between 2 and 3 p.m. fourteen thousand people went through Barnsley Toll Bar. The crowd formed at the entrance to the pit, where the

Rev. J. Oddy handed out religious material. On the following Wednesday another explosion occurred, obscuring the pit and houses in a cloud of dense smoke. So violent was the explosion that the timber which covered the shaft mouth was hurled into the head gear. The door of the engine house was blown off its hinges and the room filled with smoke. An artist from the *Illustrated London News* was sketching a group of men when the explosion occurred and he quickly took flight.

One man named Frobisher left a widow and three step children, the father of whom had been one of the victims of the Darley Main disaster in 1849. It was said Worsbrough Common had 18 houses in mourning and that other victims came from Worsbrough Dale and Berry Brow.

An expert said later that the quantity of gas in the pit was increased by the unjustifiable rapidity with which the coal was excavated, the men working in shifts day and night, spurred on by a bonus of £1 per team if they excavated fifty yards a fortnight. He said a blast of gunpowder fired gas four days before the explosion and was again fired by a candle on December 6th when men worked for nearly an hour to put the fire out.

In January 1863, the following letter appeared in a local newspaper:

"I doubt whether in the annals of colliery atrocities a blacker case is recorded than that of Edmund's Main. The person charged with the direction of the workings when the first explosion occurred seems to have played with life with as little concern as a child

Chapter 6
Filling the gaps

Baskets were used to bring coal to the surface before the 1800s. Later, however, steam power was introduced and coal put in trucks which were then wound to the surface. The next stage involved sophisticated shaft cages to carry the trucks and men.

▢▢▢▢

As early as 1700 three quarters of a million tons were exported by ship from the north east, mainly to the London market. The sea-borne trade of London was overtaken by the railways in 1867 but by 1913 coastal shipments, at more than nine million tons, were greater than rail movements but thereafter the trade declined.

▢▢▢▢

The 1841 Miners' Association of Great Britain reached 100,000 members but the success of the union failed in the face of the greater power of the owners. The Miners' Federation of Great Britain was formed in 1889; yet only two thirds of the work force was unionised by 1900.

▢▢▢▢

Tinkering with death . . . miners and management often disregarded safety. In the 1840s a Barnsley miner, E. A. Rymer, author of *Martyrdom of the Mines* (1896), and who died in 1915, said he used to make small holes in the coal and shove in pipe stopples, set fire to the gas and play with the flames. *"I have worked in places with sufficient gas around which, if it had exploded, would have blown up the mine."*

▢▢▢▢

It's not surprising that in the early days of mining some miners preferred to work in the dark, for the attempts at lighting were crude. Flaming torches, crude oil lamps and tallow candles were common, often resulting in explosions. So attempts were made to illuminate mines without actual flame. The devices: phosphorescent fish skins, mirrors reflecting lights from the top of the shaft and later the Spedding

Flint Mill. This device was carried by a boy who accompanied the collier and produced a shower of sparks by turning the toothed wheel of the mill which rubbed against a flint. In the early 1800s, as mines became deeper and more extensive, the explosions of fire-damp became more frequent. It had already been noted that an inflammable gas was often present in closed workings, a gas which was apparently lighter than air, since it lodged in roof cavities. To try to improve the conditions, the "fireman" (see illustration), clothed in wet sacking, crawled along the floor and raised a lighted candle tied to a pole into the cavity. The gas ignited and burned with a bluish flame and was termed

Below: The most dangerous job in the pit . . . the fireman tests for gas.

fire-damp. When the workings had become linked and the air circulated, the gas still lodged in the cavities, and the fireman tried to deal with it in the usual manner, but instead of quiet combustion there was often a violent explosion. In 1813 Dr. Clanny invented the first safety lamp and an improved safety lamp was later produced by Humphrey Davey. At the beginning of this century naked lights were still used in some shallow mines. Even mining engineers said that naked lights provided a better light, resulting in fewer roof falls and greater productivity. Today deputies are asked to test for fire-damp in the general body of the air, in roadways, working places and in the main and branch airways for accumulations of gas at the coal face, any blind end and in any break.

□□□□

As areas became more populous, it became necessary to avoid those methods of shallow seam mining which caused extensive subsidence and damage on the surface. This, combined with the lack of knowledge of roof control, led to the adoption of the remained pillar system of mining. This consisted of driving headings in the seam so as to form coal pillars (see illustration). Where surface support was required, pillars of coal of requisite size were left.

□□□□

In 1857 two miners, Bromley and Walker broke open a solid block of coal at Darley Main Colliery, Worsbrough, and inside found a living toad with no mouth. According to Wilkinson's History of Wors-

brough, the toad lived for a few hours in a case in the manager's office. Experts dismissed the story as either a hoax or as a mistake, pointing out that the toad had come down the shaft and the men had made a mistake in the dark.

□□□□

The Silkstone Colliery at Higham exploded in 1858. A man called Cooper was the only workman in the pit at the time because the pit was closed on the Day of Humiliation (Indian Mutiny), otherwise many lives could have been lost. Ten pit ponies were killed and the surface premises damaged. The report of the explosion was heard for miles around.

□□□□

In the 1850s a workman could not change his job until he had received clearance from his employer, who had to sign a note saying he had left such and such a firm in a proper and lawful manner. Cases like the following were frequent: at the Barnsley Court House, T. Denton, of Dodworth, who left the employment of G. W. Clarke, of Silkstone Fall Colliery without the necessary notice was ordered to go to work his notice out, or pay a fine. The expenses of the court were deducted from his wages.

□□□□

In the 1870s seven hundred men were employed at Day's pits, Mount Osborne, the Rosa, the Old Mill and Agnes. At Mount Osborne the manager was a Mr. Muckle.

□□□□

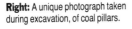

Right: A unique photograph taken during excavation, of coal pillars.

Pit ponies were roasted alive when a fire broke out at Darfield Main Colliery in October, 1872. When the buzzer rang out on Sunday night, scores of people turned up at the pit to see what had happened. The air had reversed in the cupola shaft and water was pouring into the pit. The only man in the pit bottom at the time was John Mitchell, the furnaceman. The fire in the furnace had spread because the air had been reversed, and had ignited a considerable amount of slack used for firing: he saw no fewer than thirty seven corves ablaze. The chair used for raising and lowering the men was drawn up and was found to be red hot. There were forty five horses and ponies down the pit, all of which were roasted alive. Soon all cabins and headgear were a mass of flames as the fire came up the drawing shaft, the distance to the top being three hundred and thirty seven yards. The flames rose forty to fifty yards above the raised platform, illuminating the surrounding countryside. Fire engines arrived from Barnsley and water was drawn from the reservoir of Mr. H. Garland, of Wood Hall. The blaze took hours to control. A journalist wrote: *"The appearance of the top was desolate, the platform and its surroundings being a complete wreck. It is impossible to estimate the amount of the damage. The colliery produces from six hundred to seven hundred tons of coal daily and between four hundred and five hundred hands will be thrown out of employment. The horses are valued at about £1,500."*

▢▢▢▢

Singular and amusing hoax near Barnsley — that's how *The Barnsley Illustrated Weekly* of 1874 described an incident during a strike at Church Lane Colliery, Dodworth. The reporter wrote: *"It will be remembered that the miners at the colliery have been on strike against the award of an umpire. Early on Friday morning between twenty and thirty people got off the train at Dodworth Station and were seen to go to the colliery accompanied by Mr. Hickson, the mining engineer. The men who were on the look-out at once concluded that they were the new hands, or 'black sheep' as they are termed. An adjourned meeting was fixed to be held in Barnsley the same morning at ten o'clock. All the speakers who addressed the meeting dwelt upon the arrival of the 'black sheep' from Lancashire. One speaker said he was more amused at their appearance than annoyed because they looked like men who would not do much work, as they had gone down the pit in their 'Sunday best.' The speakers spoke about the appearance of the 'new hands' and begged their companions to keep the peace. On leaving the pit, the 'fresh hands' received the attention of the females in the community. On Saturday the officials of the colliery were surprised at the reports in some of the newspapers, and it then transpired that the men were none other than a number of the members of a Lancashire Colliery Managers' Association, who were on a visit to the leading collieries in the district. Amongst other collieries which they visited were the New Oaks, Darfield Main and the Buzzards Colliery,* near Hoyland Nether. *These gentlemen, who were managers of some of the largest collieries in Wigan, Manchester, and other districts, did not know they had appeared in a new character until the evening of the same day, when they returned to Barnsley and became acquainted with what had taken place.*

▢▢▢▢

High wages attracted prostitutes to pits. A local newspaper carried the following court story in 1874: *"Kate Hirst was charged with being in a public place and behaving in an indecent manner at Barnsley on June 7, Police constable Gorden said he was sent for by the manager at Mount Osborne Colliery and he went down and found the defendant with several youths, keeping them loitering. There were also several men nearby who appeared to be waiting for her. Ordered to leave the town."*

▢▢▢▢

A miner was killed at Smithies in 1874. *"Gross insult was committed on his family and on the mourners by the wilful neglect of both the Vicar and the curate,"* wrote Rymer. Torches had to be used to bury the corpse in the cemetery at night. The family protested to the Archbishop of York and the local ministers, who had been involved in a Parliamentary election on the day of the funeral, were removed to other parishes.

▢▢▢▢

Extract from a Barnsley newspaper of 1874 *"On Tuesday an important meeting of delegates connected with the South Yorkshire and North Derbyshire Miners' Association was held in the Temperance Hall, Barnsley, for the purpose of considering the second proposal made by the colliery owners, as to accepting a reduction of wages to the extent of ten per cent on the gross earnings. There were upwards of 100 delegates, representing about 24,000 miners. In the first instance it will be remembered that the masters asked for a reduction of twelve and a half per cent on the present earnings, to which, on the part of the men, it was agreed to accept ten per cent from the advances made since 1871, or from the then prices. This was refused by the colliery owners, seeing that it was exactly only half of what was required, being only six and three quarter per cent of gross earnings. At a subsequent meeting held by the mine owners a reduction of ten per cent of existing earnings was proposed. The meeting on Tuesday was held for the purpose of considering the proposal, when it appeared that there was a considerable change in the delegates sent by several of the lodges, many of those who attended the previous meeting having being charged with voting against their instructions. After considerable discussion the proposition submitted at the last meeting for a reduction of ten per cent on the earnings of 1871, or in advances since made, was agreed to. The proposal of the masters was not accepted. (A circular issued to members was signed John Normansell, Philip Casey, Nelson Street, Barnsley)."*

Another newspaper report stated: *"During the*

discussion (at Tuesday's meeting) attention was drawn to the fact that the much-talked-of advance of seventy five per cent (in the price of coal) only increased the colliers' wages by about 8d. per ton in the Barnsley district. On the other hand the colliery proprietors who supplied Barnsley now charged 15s. per ton for the same for which they only obtained about 9s. per ton in 1871. Thus whilst the colliers' wages had increased 8d. per ton since 1871, the colliery owners at Barnsley were getting 6s. per ton more for their coal than they did that year. In reply it was stated that there were about three colliery firms in Barnsley that monopolised the trade of that town, and whilst they were able to charge 15s. a ton for the coal delivered, the largest owners in the district sending by railway were unable to get more than 10s. or 11s. per ton. The result is looked forward to with a great deal of interest, as it is considered that a lock-out — at some places at least — is not improbable."

□□□□

Anyone who thinks the world isn't what it used to be should examine the local newspapers in the last century. On one page of a Barnsley newspaper of 1874 there were stories about a Hoyland man trying to shoot his sweetheart; a fraud case involving a trustee of the Lily of the Valley Lodge of the Independent Order of Oddfellows; assaults on wives at Dodworth and Monk Bretton; an attack on a policeman and the usual *"fatal accident at Barnsley colliery"* (see Accidents and Explosions).

"On Monday, at 5.30 a.m., John Bennett, living at Worsbrough Common, was killed, and Samuel Simmons was seriously injured, by the fall of stone from the roof of Agnes Colliery. Both men were finishing work as labourers on the night shift when the accident occurred. Bennett, who leaves a widow and eight small children, was killed on the spot. Simmons, who is also married, is seriously cut about the head. He has been many times seriously injured, and was only just recovering from a similar serious accident."

There was also this peculiar story: *"Alarming gunpowder explosion at Royston. On Tuesday, a curious and alarming explosion of gunpowder, by which three persons were seriously injured, occurred at Royston. The incidents relating to the accident are of a peculiar character. It appears that a new colliery is being sunk in the neighbourhood of Ryhill, a village near Royston. From some cause or other the sinkers fell short of blasting powder and a young man named Edward Schofield, who is employed at the pit, was sent to Staincross. Here he appears to have secured 16lb of gunpowder, which he put in a bag, and getting a stick, slung it over his shoulder. On his road to Ryhill he had to pass through Royston., and here he called at the blacksmith's shop, owned by Chas Pickard. At the time Schofield entered the shop with the dangerous compound on his back, Pickard and his apprentice were busy making horse shoes. The hot iron was taken from the smithy fire; no sooner had they started to beat the iron than Schofield turned*

his back on the red hot sparks. The powder became ignited and a serious explosion took place. The smithy had a large door and the explosion was not confined, or the whole place would have been blown up. All the occupants of the smithy were seriously burnt, but it is thought they are not seriously injured. The sufferers are as well as they can be expected. It is wonderful how they escaped being killed on the spot."

□□□□

Relief funds: the first fund to be opened in Barnsley followed the first Oaks explosion in 1847, when £2,308 was raised for the widows and orphans of the 73 victims. About £50,000 was raised for the dependents in the Oaks disaster in 1866. That sum included a Bank of England £1,000 note received from a donor who signed himself "A-Z." In 1875 the following paragraph appeared in a newspaper: *"Mr. Attwood died recently aged about 80. He was a rich bachelor, the anonymous donor of £1,000 cheques and bank notes. His books shew he gave away £350,000 — £35,000 in the last year. A £1,000 note was found lying about the room as if it was waste paper."*

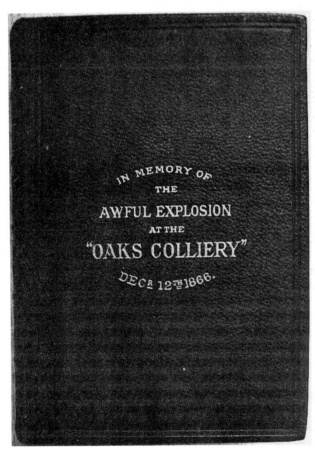

One of the prime movers behind the formation of the West Riding Miners' Relief Fund, set up in 1877, was the Rev. H. J. Day, the Rector of Barnsley, who addressed meetings of miners to try to persuade them to contribute to the fund. Mr. Day pointed out that the disasters caught the headlines but miners were killed or seriously injured in accidents every week and their families needed financial support. The first fortnight's subscriptions amounted to £45. Membership of the fund soon grew as miners realised the

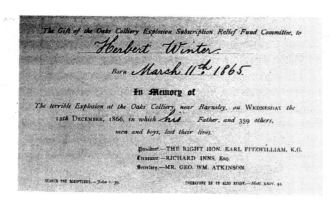

The Gift of the Oaks Colliery Explosion Subscription Relief Fund Committee, to

Herbert Winter.

Born *March 11th 1865.*

In Memory of

The terrible Explosion at the Oaks Colliery, near Barnsley, on WEDNESDAY the 12th DECEMBER, 1866, in which *his* Father, and 359 others, men and boys, lost their lives.

President—THE RIGHT HON. EARL FITZWILLIAM, K.G.
Treasurer—RICHARD INNS, Esq.
Secretary—MR. GEO. WM. ATKINSON.

SEARCH THE SCRIPTURES.—*John* v. 39.   THEREFORE BE YE ALSO READY.—*Matt.* XXIV. 44.

advantages. The largest branches were Wombwell Main (281 members), New Oaks (225), Swaithe Main (183), Pindar Oaks (142), and Woolley (107). The first committee consisted of Sam Lambert (Wombwell Main), W. Jackson (Edmund's Main), Edward Jones (Old Oaks), J. Bostock (Swaithe Main), C. Tipping (Pindar Oaks), John Fairhurst (North Gawber), C. Wroe (Cooper's Colliery), Henry Cooper (Wharncliffe Silkstone), J. Wilcock (Day Colliery), Henry Neville (Mitchell Main), George Gomersall (Blacker Main) and George Clarke (Lundhill).

Mines Inspectors generally went out of their way to praise the courage of miners, whom they regarded as a special breed of men. Criticism was unusual but this item appeared in the local inspector's report for 1878: *"In January (1877), a man called Wilkinson was killed at Lundhill Colliery, Wombwell, and a man called Fletcher was buried for one and a half hours. The conduct of some of the men was utterly at variance with the usual heroism and disregard of danger displayed by miners under similar circumstances and affords a marked contrast to the qualities which as a rule characterise them."*

In 1884 the Mines Inspector said he wanted to express his satisfaction and thankfulness that he had not to chronicle any disaster involving large loss of life. But he added: *"It is a fact and, unfortunately, one which science and experience have not as yet been able to remove that a mine which may have been examined from end to end and found free of gas is liable in the next minute, without warning, to be rendered highly dangerous by reason of one of the sudden emissions of gas. In one instance, the issue of gas was of such a nature that a flow of twenty seven thousand cubic feet of air per minute, set apart for no other object than to dilute the gas, is almost powerless to deal with it."*

Yorkshire miners' galas served a four fold purpose, according to Demonstrations, The Pride of the Yorkshire Miners, by Sam Thompson, and published by the Yorkshire NUM two years ago. *"They brought together men from widely separated branches and gave them and the general public a clearer idea of the strength and importance of the Miners' Union,"* wrote Mr. Thompson. *"They also provided the secretary with an opportunity to outline the position and standing of the association and the future prospects of the district; they were made the occasion for a review of the weaknesses and shortcomings of existing Acts of Parliament relating to the mining industry and for suggestions to improve such legislation; and for the airing of projects in which the miners were interested."*

Extract from the Barnsley Independent, 1890: *"On the evening following the conclusion of the speeches a gala was held in the Queen's Ground. A large number of people from the country as well as the towns paid for admission, in fact no fewer than twelve thousand people passed through the turnstiles. There were various attractions including Nimrod, the Cannon-ball King, who gave some very clever performances; Mikado the Great Juggler, and the Paynes, comic and artistic skaters. The chief feature of the evening, however, was the balloon ascent and parachute descent by Miss Cissie Kent, England's Lady Parachutist, who some weeks ago made a successful aerial flight in the town. The ascent was announced to take place at six o'clock and by that time the ground was packed by people.*

"Miss Kent made her way through the crowd and received the most flattering reception. She was dressed in a blue velvet suit with a navy blue and white spotted handkerchief tied round her head in turban fashion, wearing high top boots and looking the picture of health. The balloon was well inflated and rolled buoyantly in consequence of the strong wind. In a short time the words 'Let's go' were heard and Miss Kent, in the balloon with her parachute, rose rapidly to a height of about ten thousand feet sailing towards Cudworth. For a time all her movements were plainly visible and at the altitude named, she was seen preparing for the drop. She threw herself off the seat and in a few seconds the parachute was seen to open, greatly to the relief of the spectators. The time from leaving the ground to the disconnection from the balloon was exactly five and a half minutes, and the drop occupied twelve and a half minutes, the longest we understand the parachutist has ever experienced. The dark clouds through which she had to pass for a time hid Miss Kent from view, but when she again became visible she seemed to be rapidly swinging to and fro, the descent being evidently a troublesome one. She, however, alighted safely near Mr. John Guest's farm at Long Houghton. She was all right."

From the Independent, 1897: *"The Yorkshire Miners' Association increases its influence year by year, and as a consequence, the annual demonstration increases in popularity as each successive year comes round. Barnsley may claim to be the favourite rendezvous of the miners for their yearly gathering, and after three years the Association came back to the capital of the South Yorkshire Coalfield. The collier is proverbially a philosopher. In hard times as well as good times the Yorkshire miner can enjoy their demonstration — a function in which business*

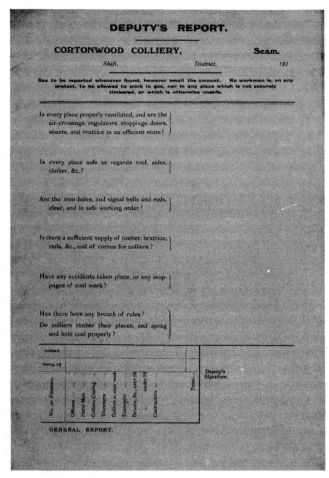

travelling a road containing damp. It is usually easier to go forward than to return, as in going forward the gas which lies near the floor is stirred up, making the return journey much more difficult.

Carbonic Oxide or Carbon Monoxide: *"This gas is not given off naturally in mines, but results from incomplete combustion. Whenever carbon is burned in an insufficient supply of oxygen, carbon monoxide is formed. It may result from a gob-fire, from blasting when the explosive is bad, and from an explosion of gas and coal-dust. It is an extremely dangerous gas. Dr. Haldane, who has investigated the subject very thoroughly, suggests that a live mouse should be taken into the mine after an explosion has occurred. A mouse suffers from the same symptoms as a man, but the effect is much more rapid.*

Sulphuretted hydrogen: *"This gas is generated by the putrefaction of animal and vegetable matter, and by the oxidation of sulphates. It is sometimes found in old water-levels and in old workings which have been filled with water. It is highly poisonous.*

After-damp: *"The mixture of gases which results from an explosion of gas, or of gas and coal-dust, is known as after-damp. The composition of after-damp depends on the proportions of gas, air, and coal-dust which take part in the explosion. According to Dr. Haldane, the chief cause of death in colliery explosions is the presence of carbon monoxide. He found that in three great explosions seventy seven per cent of the men killed were not killed by the force of the blast, but by the after-damp, and their bodies showed every symptom of death by carbon monoxide poisioning.*

The furnace: *"Furnaces are now never built to ventilate important collieries, fans being preferred. There are, however, many old but large collieries in the north and elsewhere which are efficiently ventilated by furnaces. In many of the old collieries steam is generated underground, and the waste heat from the boilers contributes largely to the ventilation of the mine. A ventilating furnace in conjunction with underground boilers is probably the cheapest method of ventilating a deep mine, but the advantages are more than balanced by the great inconvenience, and by the element of danger that is introduced by having fires underground.*

Safety lamps: *"A safety-lamp should be absolutely incapable of firing an explosive mixture under any possible combination of circumstances which occur underground; it should give a fair light throughout the whole shift, even when used in districts where the air current is sluggish and impure, and it should be simple in design and easy to clean. Safety-lamps depend for their security upon the fact that fire-damp will not explode until exposed to a certain temperature, which is known as the temperature of ignition, and that when a flame has passed through a wire-gauze it is cooled down by the wires to below the temperature of ignition."*

Privies and middens

A fascinating as well as a sombre and amusing insight into life in Goldthorpe and Bolton-on-Dearne at the turn of the century is given in the Medical Officer of Health's annual reports. The mining villages, overcrowded and expanding at an alarming rate, were plagued by clouds of smoke that obscured the sun; high infant mortality rates and residents who kept pigs in the back yards and who didn't know how to use lavatories. The humans, that is.

In his first report, in 1900, the M.O.H. for Bolton Council took an instant dislike to back yards and pit chimneys:

"Many yards do not have grates to take away the water. This, coupled with the clayey nature of the soil

Opposite page: Deputies testing the roof and for gas.
Photograph: Yorkshire Mining Museum/Leeds City Museum.

Left: A deputies report form from Cortonwood Colliery.

Below: The men who had to collect the night-soil. Pictured in Birdwell at the turn of the century.

renders back yards in wet weather almost ankle-deep in mud. In many places about Main Street and Packey's Puzzle tenants of the houses take no pride whatever in keeping their yards clean and tidy but throw all their household rubbish about the yards. Decomposing vegetables and animal refuse are a very potent danger to health."

And he urged by-laws against the accumulation of hutches, fowl runs, small sheds and piggeries in the court yards. Commenting on atmospheric pollution, he wrote:

"Pits are pouring out large volumes of smoke, often two miles in length. You get smoke obscuring the sun and blackening everything. I think it is time to put pressure on the owners to diminish the smoke."

To add insult to injury, none of the offending pits were in the urban district, thus robbing the council of much needed income from rates.

In his 1901 report, he said one in seven children died before reaching twelve months, due to infantile diarrhoea and other diseases, and there were cases of typhoid in the villages. Fortunately, there were no cases of small-pox, mainly because Bolton and Goldthorpe were isolated and because there were no lodging houses for tramps who might carry the disease into the districts. Then he criticised the back yards again:

"Wooden erections are preventing the free circulation of air in back yards and some yards have evil smelling swill tubs."

Before dustbins were widely introduced, ashes and rubbish were dumped in ash-pits in yards. He complained:

"I doubt if there is in the whole of Goldthorpe one ash-pit more than two years old which does not have a broken door or grate to it. Anything and everything goes into the ash-pit. In the summer the contents are a seething mass of corruption covered by swarms of flies. Fowls and children often go straight from the ash-pit with filth on their feet into the houses!"

In his 1904 report, he noted that there were six deaths from *"white man's plague,"* consumption of the lungs, four of which occurred in Main Street, Goldthorpe, the most crowded street where fresh air was scarcest and then he added:

"I am pleased to report that fewer pigs are kept in back yards, several piggeries having been cleared as a result of the recent epidemic of enteric fever. Our slop water closets have continued to act very well except where the tenants have misused them. Where they have been used as dustbins they have of course become a great nuisance."

The population was nearly 5,000 but there were only 109 water closets:

"Tenants from houses where privy middens are used, on taking houses where water closets are in use, persist for a time in using the seat as a dust bin, as they have been accustomed to do so."

On infant mortality, in his 1908 report, he commented:

"The child feeds as we do, is the expression often used about a six months old baby. But bottle feeding is often a fruitful source of death. The bottle with a long India rubber tube is a death trap. It can never be perfectly clean, particularly when it is passed from mouth to mouth. A filthy house is another death trap. How many mothers in Goldthorpe have the house cleaned-up, or wear a nice white apron, in time for the arrival of their husbands from work? When we look at some of the houses and see the filthy conditions, the complete absence of comfort can we wonder that so many husbands spend their evenings amid the lights, the cosy fireside and the cleanliness and comfort of public houses and their working men's clubs? Drunkenness is another great cause of infantile mortality, not necessarily in the mother but in the father, causing a child with a weak constitution. Flies and privy middens are another."

He recommended more water closets and fewer

Right: Keeping the back steps clean must have been a full time job for the families who lived close to the pits.

middens; more paved yards; better motherhood; greater cleanliness in the home and provision of a district nurse.

By 1908, 151 water closets were in use and ash-pits continued to be a problem. Many ash-pit doors had disappeared.

"This state of affairs is treated lightly by property owners. Dogs and cats frequent these places and children play hide and seek in them. Apart from the want of decency, it is most important that these should be remedied immediately. A child nurses a cat regardless of where it has been."

The M.O.H. at Hoyland had similar problems. In his 1913 report he said there were 133 baths in a total of 3,000 houses.

"It can be presumed that the facilities for personal cleanliness in many of our inferior cottages are conspicuous by their absence. In addition, the amount of dirt and dust in a coal miner's cottage is largely increased, which necessitates washing of persons and clothes. The awkward hours of work and the difference in the meal times of the workers and children attending school causes the wife much more work and renders her lot in life no soft job. Overworked mothers become disheartened, standards of cleanliness are lowered. Many back yards are in a filthy condition, covered with faecal matter of the

children owing to the parents being either too lazy or too careless to see and enforce the children to use the proper places, instead of letting them squat in the back yard. In addition to this problem, the yard is often the dwelling place of poultry, rabbits and dogs, all polluting the soil."

The M.O.H. quoted a doctor as saying:

"In the case of mining areas the responsibility for inferior housing is divided between the sanitary authorities, colliery owners and the miners themselves. The latter receive relatively high wages but content themselves with grossly inferior houses. Until they are willing to spend considerably larger portions of their weekly earnings in high rents, progress will not be made."

Then the M.O.H. referred to the worst form of nuisance, the wheeling and tipping of night soil (human excreta) from privies into the streets. Nearly 200 cases were reported in 1912, 25 of which were in Cherry Tree Street, Elsecar.

The vast strides made in public health can be seen when you compare the old Bolton-on-Dearne health reports with the report for 1926. The death rate in 1903 had been 23.48 per thousand; the death rate 23 years later was the lowest ever recorded, thanks to low infant mortality rates. Almost all the houses had water closets by 1926.

Above: This photograph taken in the north east illustrates what conditions were like at Goldthorpe and Bolton-on-Dearne in 1909. Public health officials turned a blind eye to overcrowding because there was a shortage of houses.
Photograph: Beamish, North of England Open Air Museum.

CHAS. CAMMELL AND COMPY LTD

OLD & NEW OAKS COLLIERIES

NR BARNSLEY

Charles Cammell and Co., Cyclops Works, Sheffield who owned the Old (Hoyle Mill) and New Oaks (Stairfoot) Collieries, produced a photographic record of their premises (above and opposite). **Above:** Top left, New Oaks; top right, the Old Oaks; centre, a view of the Old Oaks colliery from the new railway sidings; bottom left, a battery of boilers from the Old Oaks; bottom right, the New Oaks from the railway.
Below: An illustration of the Old Oaks Colliery.

CHAS CAMMELL AND COMPY LTD

OLD & NEW OAKS COLLIERIES

Nr BARNSLEY

DEPUTIES HOUSES NEW OAKS COLLIERY.

NEW OAKS OFFICES AND UNDER MANAGER'S HOUSE.

GENERAL VIEW OF NEW OAKS COLLIERY FROM CANAL BANK

REAR VIEW NEW OAKS COLLIERY.

NEW OAKS FROM THE OFFICES.

Above: Views of the New Oaks Colliery, Stairfoot. Top left, deputy row; top right, offices and under manager's house; centre, pit viewed from the canal bank; bottom left, rear view of pit; bottom right, from the offices.

Below: Illustration of the New Oaks Colliery.

Right: Young lads getting the coal in, a familiar sight throughout the streets of Barnsley.

Below: By the early years of this century Barnsley was reaching its peak as the coal capital of South Yorkshire, and as a shopping centre for the surrounding mining villages.

Chapter 8
The 1920s and 30s

1920s

The General Strike and the miners' lock-out marked a watershed in the history of the miners and in British post-war history. The lock-out was also significant because it had striking parallels with the 1984/85 strike.

The root causes of the 1926 dispute were the almost malignant suspicion and the traditional antagonism between the coal owners and miners, and the aftermath of the First World War. The nineteenth century had been riddled with long and bitter strikes and lock-outs in which both sides refused to give an inch. When times were bad, the owners demanded — and got — lower wages and longer hours; when times were good miners demanded higher wages and often got them after a fight.

After the war, the owners were still smarting from the miners' victories in 1893 and 1912 when the unions appeared to gain the upper hand. Also, the owners did not like the eight hour day, introduced in 1907,

which had led to lower production. To add to the industry's problems, the world markets had changed. In 1913, of the three chief coal exporting countries, Great Britain exported 98.7 million tonnes, Germany 34.5 million and the USA 28 million. During the war exports fell, prompting other countries to develop their coal deposits, or to seek coal elsewhere.

In 1918, at the end of the war, industrial trouble broke out again. Miners had assumed that Government control of the mines in the war was the first step towards nationalisation, a cherished ideal. In 1921 there was a lock-out following the decontrol of the mines and two years later there was a move in Parliament to nationalise the pits but without any success. At the same time demand for coal was falling, as was production (in 1922 each miner produced 223 tons, compared with 259 in 1913), and wages were failing to keep up with the cost of living.

All the ingredients were there for another explosion. The fuse was lit when the owners came up with the old formula to solve the short-term problems

Above and below: Mr. Herbert Smith, Yorkshire Miners' leader, pictured at Whit 'Sing' near North Gawber Colliery, 1920s.

of the industry — lower wages and longer hours. Whereas in the past miners had stood alone, this time there was a chance that other unions would support them, for many trade union leaders thought miners were the most ill-used of workers.

In the view of the militants, a General Strike would paralyse the country and probably bring down the Government, helping to usher in an age of Socialism and the destruction of the hated capitalist system.

Other trade unionists were afraid of the power in their hands; at any rate a General Strike was not the way the British did things.

As in 1984, the Government were not taken unawares. In 1924 they had backed off from a confrontation with the miners in order to organise and prepare essential services in the event of a General Strike. The Government were also aware that coal stocks were high and that industry could ride out the storm.

The General Strike, called to support the miners in their battle to maintain existing wages and working hours, lasted only nine days, from May 3rd to May 12th, 1926. It has been described as the most widespread and dramatic breakdown of Britain's industrial relations for a century. Not all workers were on strike — only the railwaymen, builders, printers, engineers, transport, ship-yard and iron and steel workers joined in. Many people, including undergraduates, had the time of their lives driving trains and buses while the strike lasted. The unions had never prepared for such a strike; the leaders pursued it hesitantly; and they were frightened of opening Pandora's Box. To take on the State, you have to trigger off a revolution and trade union leaders were not prepared to pull the trigger. The strike collapsed.

When the other unions went back to work, the miners struggled on for months. As in 1984, the Government and the employers were unyielding. So were the miners. Lord Birkenhead said he thought he had never met anyone as stupid as a miners' leader until he met a coal owner.

As in the recent miners' strike, the miners of Nottinghamshire broke away from the federation and set up their own union. Even the weather was similar.

Below: A Barnsley soup kitchen team pictured during the 1926 lock-out.

Left: Lundhill Chapel in the 1920s. The pit had gone but the houses, the pub and the chapel remained. The Chapel was used as a mortuary in the 1857 disaster. Joe Hall, the miners' leader, was 'educated' at the chapel.

Photograph: Joe Short.

Below: Barnsley Salvation Army soup kitchen in 1921.

MINERS STRIKE 1921
SALVATION ARMY · BARNSLEY
SOUP KITCHEN
COOKS AND ASSISTANTS
300 TO 500 FREE DINNERS
DAILY

Daily Herald

No. 6390   FRIDAY, AUGUST 7, 1936   ONE PENNY

Barnsley Pit Explosion

57 MINERS HURLED TO DEATH IN A FLASH

THE REV. NORMAN KING, vicar of Carlton, Barnsley, praying, with watchers at the pithead of the imprisoned men. (Other pictures on Back Page.)

MINE LAMPS GUIDE CORTEGE

From Our Special Correspondent

BARNSLEY, Friday morning.

EARLY to-day a crowd still waited outside the school which has been turned into a mortuary to receive the dead.

Miners' lamps were placed along the path leading to it, and the light flickered eerily in the breeze to guide the stretcher-bearers bringing the victims from the ambulances.

Pitiful scenes were witnessed when police and doctors who had made a pre-

Daily Herald Free Insurance

THE comprehensive free insurance provided by the "Daily Herald" for its registered readers includes benefits for all fatal accidents.

Inquiries are being made and as soon as any of the victims of the Barnsley disaster are identified as registered readers of the "Daily Herald," cheques will be sent immediately to their dependents.

liminary examination of the bodies, arrived at provisional identification.

When they thought they had identified a man, a police officer came out and asked the waiting men and women if there were any among them who were related to —— mentioning a name.

Every time this happened, someone answered "Yes," and went into the schoolroom to view a body. In this way the identification of the victims is being completed.

PAPER BLINDS

Inside the schoolroom miners' lamps hung from brackets on the wall. Sheets of brown paper were placed across the windows as blinds.

Yesterday morning there was a pithead service, led by the Rev. Norman King, vicar of the village of Carlton.

The Lord's Prayer was recited. Men around the pithead took off their caps. Women closed their eyes.

ONLY ONE MAN KNOWS HOW IT HAPPENED

Wives See Bodies Brought Up

FROM OUR SPECIAL CORRESPONDENTS
BARNSLEY, Yorks, Thursday.

FIFTY-SEVEN bodies, some of them twisted and battered beyond recognition, are to-night being slowly borne from the Wharncliffe Woodmoor Colliery, shaken this morning by one of the worst mine explosions this county has known.

Along a private road at the back of the pit, ambulances are moving through the darkness to the quaint, disused church school of Carlton, the village in which the colliery stands.

A knot of women, drawn-faced, wide-eyed, are grouped around, silent in the pitiless rain. . . .

So far, 33 bodies have been brought to the surface—many by volunteer stretcher-bearers, who came forward in answer to an appeal by the management.

"There is not the slightest chance," I am told, "of anyone being found alive."

The task of recovering the victims will be resumed at 6 a.m. to-morrow.

EFFECTS SEEN
A MILE AWAY

THE explosion—some accounts say there were more than one—was so dreadful that its effects were to be seen more than a mile from the spot at which it took place—nearly two miles along an underground railway.

One man alone lived through that devastating second of death and destruction.

He is an engineman, Alfred Brown, of Smithies, Barnsley; and he is so shockingly injured that he has not yet been able to speak.

Brown was found, bruised and battered, 1,800 yards from where the explosion happened. That shows the merciless ferocity with which death came to his comrades.

WORST
SINCE GRESFORD

OF the victims, 19 lived in Barnsley, 14 in Smithies, seven in Carlton and the rest in villages around.

The disaster is the worst since September, 1934, when 265 men were killed in Gresford Colliery.

You can picture the horror of the scene from the account given to me by one of the scores of gallant men who went down to see what could be done.

[Continued on Page 10; "Just a Rescue Man" and Editorial on Page Eight.]

RESCUE WORKERS at the pithead after being relieved by a fresh team.

BAREHEADED miners watching rescue workers bring a body from the pithead.

GERMANY ARMS REBELS

SENDS CARGO OF PLANES

SECRET SHIPLOAD OF BOMBERS SHOCKS BLUM CABINET

FROM OUR OWN CORRESPONDENT
PARIS, Thursday.

NEWS reached French Ministerial circles to-night that a German steamer is now on its way to Spain with a cargo of 28 bombing planes aboard.

The vessel is the 7,775-ton Usaramo, of the German East Africa Line, which left Hamburg on July 31. Pilots and mechanics accompany the planes.

The disclosure created a sensation, and was the subject of immediate informal discussion between Cabinet Ministers and political personalities of the Left.

CARRYING SHELLS, TOO

It is known that before leaving for the south the steamer called at Emden and completed its cargo with bombs for aeroplanes, shells and machine-gun ammunition.

It leaked out from members of the crew that the steamer's destination was Spain, but they did not yet know exactly what harbour.

The ship officially bound for "the West Coast of Africa," was last reported off Ushant on Monday.

Even the strongest supporters of the "neutrality" idea begin to admit that things cannot go on any longer in this way.

A CHALLENGE

The attitude hitherto adopted by France has been that of the professional diplomat of the Quai d'Orsay. It is now openly challenged in French Trade Union quarters, and was described to me to-night by a spokesman of the French T.U.C. as "tantamount to suicide."

It was bitterly resented that the Socialist Ministers had given way to the diplomats, to the timidity of the Radical Ministers and to the blackmailing campaign of the Paris Reactionary Press.

(Other Spanish News on Page Two; Editorial on Page Eight.)

SIR D. BANKS IS NEW AIR CHIEF

LAST night 45-year-old Colonel Sir Donald Banks was working late in his office at the General Post Office, as its Director-General and business chief.

To-day he will take over command of the administrative side of the Air Ministry, as its Permanent Secretary.

For last night he was appointed to succeed Sir Christopher Bullock, whose dismissal was announced yesterday.

Sir Donald is succeeded in turn by Sir Thomas Gardiner, Deputy-Director since 1934.

Sir Christopher Bullock spent most of yesterday at his home at The Boltons, South Kensington, W. It was stated he had made no plans, but would probably leave for a holiday shortly.

(Sir D. Banks' Career, Page Four.)

GIRL TRAPPED UNDER BUS

EIGHT-TON CRANE COULD NOT SAVE LIFE

An eight-ton crane was used by London Fire Brigade last night to lift a bus in Hampstead-road, N.W., under which was trapped an 18-year-old girl cyclist, Beatrice Constance Ringe, of Great College-street, N.W.

She was dead when admitted to hospital.

MAINLY FAIR

(See Page Three)

	PAGE
Home Page	5
Postbag	6
"Just a Rescue Man," by Percy Hazel; Educate for Peace, by Mario M. Montessori; and Roundabout	8
Short Story	12
At the Pictures with P. L. Mannock; Music Notes, by Spike Hughes, T. H. Wisdom's Motoring Notes; and Radio Programmes	13

CERTIFIED DAILY NET SALES EXCEED 2,000,000

---

3 Britons Die In Alps

From Our Own Correspondent
GENEVA, Thursday.

SWISS Alps claimed two more British victims to-day—making three within the past 24 hours.

Those killed to-day were:—
Miss Martha Currant, aged 22, of Kingsbourne-green, Harpenden, Herts, and
Mr. Geoffrey C. Gregson, aged 24, believed to be from Sussex.

Miss Currant was killed while climbing with four English friends.

the 13,500ft. Matterhorn peak where Mr. George Restall, a Birmingham man, and his Swiss guide, were killed yesterday.

The party of three men and two girls had reached 12,000 feet, when a fall of rock swept Miss Currant off her feet.

Miss Currant

The rope joining her to her companions was cut by the stones, and she fell down the mountain side.

Her companions set out for help and met guides searching for the bodies of Mr. Restall and his guide.

The guides found Miss Currant dead. She had been struck on the head by stones. Her body was carried down to the valley.

She was the youngest daughter of Alderman P. W. Currant, of Luton.

Mr. Gregson and two Swiss guides were killed when a snowridge collapsed on —— b —— w— Blanche. The bridge, it is —— had been weakened by bad weather. The climbers fell over 3,000 feet.

Mr. Gregson's parents are believed to be travelling in Germany.

SIR H. PRESTON: RELAPSE

Relatives were last night summoned to the bedside of Sir Harry Preston, who is lying ill at the Royal Albion Hotel, Brighton.

He had a relapse earlier, and the official statement said: "Sir Harry's condition is serious."

BROADCAST TO BRITISH SUBJECTS

AN urgent broadcast was made at the request of the Foreign Office by the B.B.C. last night to British subjects still in Spain unable to get in touch with relatives outside.

"All are urged to communicate at once with the nearest British consular post, giving their addresses and indicating whether they are able to leave the country," said the message.

"In view of the unsettled conditions in Spain, British subjects are strongly advised to take full advantage of the facilities at present being provided for their evacuation, as these facilities cannot be held indefinitely at their disposal."

About 2,000 British have been brought away from Spain, and about 1,000 remain. Most of these have preferred to stay at their own risk, and probably only between 200 and 300 still want to be taken out.

SILENT WATCH AT THE PITHEAD

THEY REFUSED TO GIVE UP HOPE

Anxious crowds of womenfolk and comrades of the men trapped by the explosions in Wharncliffe Wood Moor Colliery, Barnsley, at the pithead, hoping for news that some, at least, of the men had been found alive.

FOR HIS MATES — An aged miner taking tea to the pithead for the rescue teams.

CHILDREN WAITED IN THE RAIN FOR HOURS

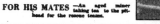

VOLUNTEER rescue workers on their way to descend the pit to face fire and roof falls in an attempt to reach the entombed men, while ambulances waited in readiness in the background.

D.338

"... like the messages carried by mysterious means over vast distances among black races, the news had spread from street to street and house to house, and soon groups of men and women from all directions were converging on the pit gates until a great crowd stood there silent ..." Jack Lawson, describing a mining tragedy. Mr. Lawson was an MP and one of his colleagues in the House of Commons in the 1950s was the Barnsley MP, and ex-miner, Lord Mason, who as a child stood in the crowd outside the gates at Wharncliffe Woodmoor, although he cannot be identified on these photographs.

Above: There is no mistaking that smile . . . entertainer George Formby is pictured at Wharncliffe Woodmoor 1,2,3 Colliery (Old Carlton) in 1936, shortly after the explosion. Formby (with helmet) is seen with the manager of the Alhambra Cinema, who organised a concert in aid of the disaster fund.
Photograph kindly loaned by Mrs. Needham, Athersley South.

Opposite page: The overhead bucket system at Monckton Colliery. Note the driver, a flat-capped youth.

Right and below:
Scenes like these were all too familiar in the 30s: *"Dead bodies were brought out feet first with a cover over the body,"* said Lord Mason, who worked at one of the Wharncliffe Woodmoor Collieries. In deep mines pressure caused air to percolate through the stone packs at roadway sides into the waste ground left by advancing faces. Gas was frequently prevalent there. The moving air engendered heat and caused fire, especially if coal or paper was left in the pack.

Above: Pit lads at Houghton Main Colliery were asked to gargle with an antiseptic solution during an epidemic of influenza.

Photo: British Coal

Right and opposite page: Programme for the 1937 Annual Demonstration of the Yorkshire Mine Workers' Association at Locke Park.

SECTION "D."—Continued.

Hemsworth Colliery Prize Band.
Hemsworth

Featherstone Subscription Band.
Snydale   Ackton Hall   South Kirkby

Frickley Colliery Prize Band.
Frickley   Brierley   Ferrymoor

Grimethorpe Colliery Prize Band.
Grimethorpe

Royston Silver Prize Band.
Monckton Main

Ryhill Prize Band.
Monckton (A)   Monk Bretton

Goldthorpe Mixed Band.
Goldthorpe   Barnbro'

Upton Band.
Upton

Y.M.A. Marshals—Mr. A. Jobling, Mr. F. Burns and Mr. W. Hewson.

Section "E."

Join at Junction of Queen Street and Peel Square.

Hickleton Main Band.
Hickleton Main

Brodsworth Prize Band.
Brodsworth Main   Hatfield Main

Bentley Prize Band.
Bentley

Bullcroft Ambulance Silver Band.
Bullcroft

Yorkshire Main Colliery Band.
Edlington   Askern Main

Rossington Miners' Welfare Band.
Rossington   Thorne

Markham Main Ambulance Band.
Armthorpe   Firbeck

Y.M.A. Marshals—Mr. F. Shaw and Mr. G. Jones.

Marshals as set out herein should report at Miners' Offices, Barnsley, at 10-0 o'clock on the morning of 21st June for final instructions.

We are, Yours truly,
H. SMITH, President.
ALF. SMITH, Agent.
J. A. HALL, Fin. Sec.
E. HOUGH, Vice-Pres.
— JONES, General Secretary.

Yorkshire Mine Workers' Association.

Registered under Trades Union Acts, 1871 to 1917.

ANNUAL

Demonstration

TO BE HELD IN THE

LOCKE PARK, BARNSLEY,

ON

MONDAY, JUNE 21st, 1937.

PLACE OF ASSEMBLY

—AND—

ORDER OF PROCESSION.

Charles Bartholomew, Esq.

Samuel Roberts, Esq.

THE
Wombwell Main Co. Ltd.
1853 — 1946

ABOUT the 20th August, 1853, it was decided by Mr. Charles Bartholomew and Mr. Samuel Roberts to sink a shaft to the Barnsley Thick Seam of coal at Wombwell, and start a concern which became known as The Wombwell Main Co. Ltd. . .

These two families, by personal contact, have directed the affairs of this Colliery during the whole of the 93 years of its existence, up to the nationalisation of the Coal Industry on 1st January, 1947. . . . . .

The present Directors hope that the successful results achieved by the team work of the Board of Directors, Officials, Staff and Men together with the atmosphere of mutual affection and respect will not easily be forgotten. . . . .

To this end we present you with this momento and wish you good luck and success for whatever may lie ahead.

C. W. Bartholomew, Esq.

The Rt. Hon.
Sir Samuel Roberts, Bart. P.C.

Major James Bartholomew, M.B.E.

Chairman of Directors.

Vice-Chairman of Directors.

Sir Samuel Roberts. Bart.

C. E. Bartholomew, Esq.

Managing Director.

Director.

Major P. G. Roberts, M.P.

STAIRFOOT

WOMBWELL LANE

EIGHT LOCKS

RAILWAY

BARNSLEY ROAD

MITCHELL MAIN SITE

ALDHAM INDUSTRIAL ESTATE

RIVER DOVE

RAILWAY

BRADBERRY BALK LANE

NETHERWOOD ROAD

Above: Visitors to Dearne Valley in 1951, including two Swedish girls. From left to right: Arthur Craven, Bob Craven, Mrs. Mavis Sharp, Colin Massingham, a Swedish girl, Mrs. Laura Smith, the second Swedish girl, Ben Nicholls and Bill Smith.
Photo: Colin Massingham

Left: "Definitely the last," says the message on the coal tub at Dearne Valley. The message may be a reference to the last hand got coal at the mine.
British Coal archives, Mansfield.

Below: No.2 underground paddy station at Dearne Valley Colliery — with the train on the left. Note the pump man's (Evans) safety lamp on the hook.
Photo: C.Massingham

Opposite page: A surveyor at work underground, probably at Grimethorpe.
Yorkshire Mining Museum.

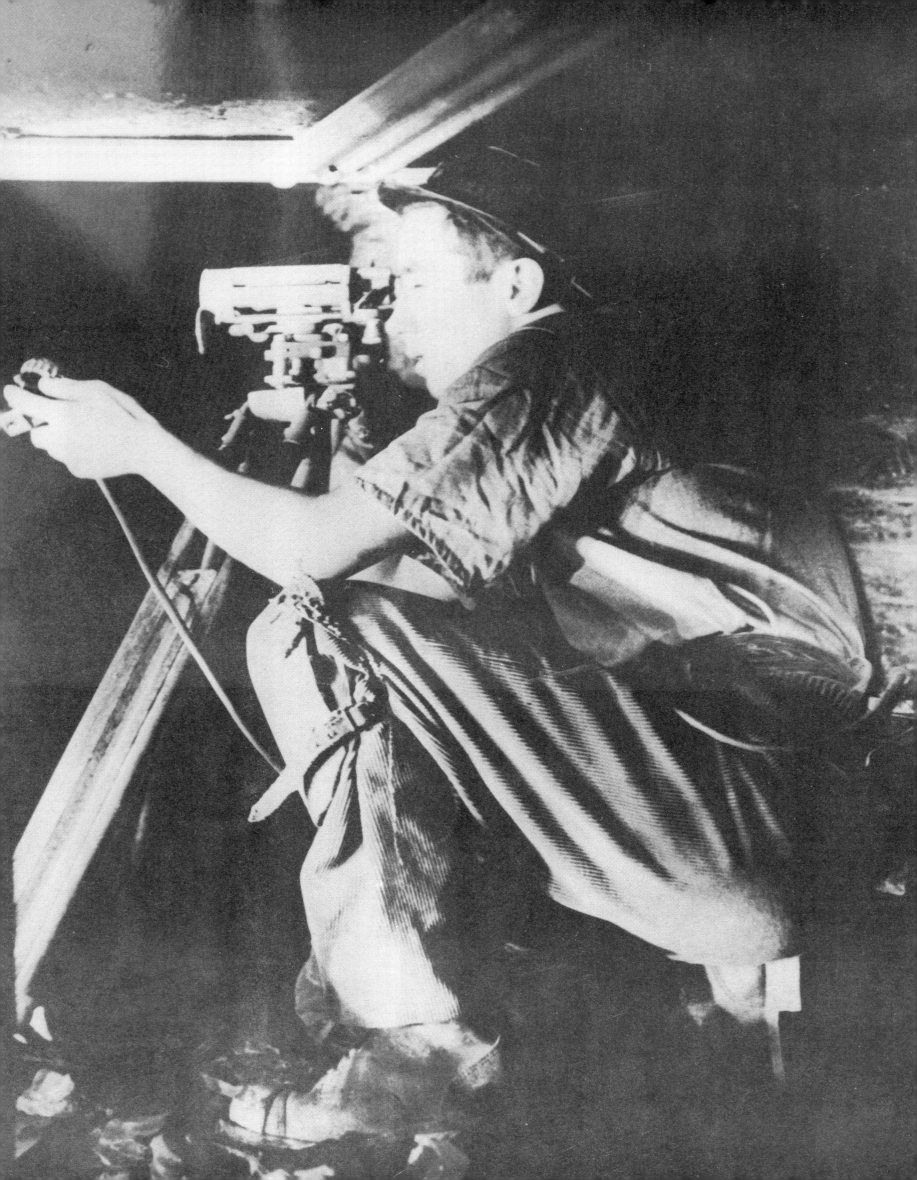

Above: Photograph of the engine house at Higham Pit taken in 1955. The engine is believed to be in a museum in Sheffield.
Left: Higham drift, 1955.
Below: Photograph of the entrance to Higham drift.
(Photographs A. Riley)

Right: Dodworth Colliery during the construction of railway sidings in 1963. The photo was taken from the railway bridge.
Below: The hoppit used at Dodworth.

Below: What must be a unique photgraph of the boring of a hole in preparation to sinking a shaft. The hole is 18 inches in diameter.

Below right: Construction of the opening to Dodworth Drift.
(Photographs A. Riley)

138

Above: A lot of hard work must have gone into preparing pit ponies for competition. This photograph shows Dodworth pit pony 'Flash' (1st prize winner) with Andrew Kirkup at Woolley Show in 1957.

(Photograph courtesy of Mr. A. Riley)

"And your job in future will be to stamp every piece of coal with N.C.B."

Above: Nationalisation of the mines in 1947 produced euphoria among miners. As early as 1884 a miners' leader had advocated nationalisation, and the establishment of the NCB was seen as a dream come true. But other people believed it was an excuse to employ layer after layer of white collar workers. This view is illustrated in this Chronicle cartoon of the time.

Right & below: Strafford Main, pictured in the 60s, when it was derelict.

Photos: A. Walker.

Above: Shuttle Eye Colliery, Nr. Flockton. Photographed in the 60s or 70s by Albert Walker.

Left: Pummer Colliery, near North Gawber Colliery.
A. Walker, Handsworth.

141

Left: Plastic meal tokens used for pit meals at Elsecar Main.
Kindly loaned by Frank Burgin
Market Street, Hoyland

Seam closed for at least 9 months following tragedy

The National Coal Board wrote off equipment worth £750,000 this week when they sealed off the Newhill seam where five men were killed in a violent explosion last Thursday night.

The decision was taken by Mr. John Kiers, the board's Barnsley area coalfield director, after consultations with union leaders.

Teams of men worked over the weekend to put permanent 17ft. thick seals on the Newhill seam and part of the adjacent Melton Field seam because of a big build up of carbon monoxide.

Tubes have been left in the seals to monitor conditions in the sealed off faces but it isn't expected that any attempt to reopen the Newhill seam will be made for at least nine months.

YORKSHIRE NUM PRESIDENT Mr. Arthur Scargill with Energy Secretary Mr. Tony Benn at Houghton Main.

Five men die in underground blast at Houghton Main

AS THE SUN SET on Thursday night, crowds of grim faced miners gathered in the yard of Houghton Main Colliery, just a short distance from the village of Little Houghton.

They had just heard that two of their workmates had died in a terrific underground explosion — 1,000 feet from the surface — that another man had serious burns, and three others were missing in the heat and dust.

The pit, which employs 1,350 men, had been cleared, and Grimethorpe Colliery, which is linked to Houghton, evacuated.

"This was a safety precaution," explained Mr. John Kiers, Area Director of the Coal Board, at a hurriedly called press conference in the pit offices.

He said: "The explosion appears to have been caused by gas. The rescue team found a big fall of roof on the main road and one of the dead men was found there."

Coaches arrived with men for the night shift, but except for two teams of hand-picked volunteers they were all sent home.

Mines rescue teams from Doncaster and Wakefield were quickly on the scene and set up their mobile units in the pit yard. Six ambulances waited near the colliery headgear.

On the warmest night of the year, families in the village chatted on the doorsteps while off-shift miners drank their pints in the open air at the working men's club, where there were relays of news from the pithead.

Pockets of men and women gathered at the entrance awaiting news of relatives. Some wives who arrived at the colliery offices were taken to a private room and given cups of tea.

As further rescue workers left the canteen after a briefing, their pit lamps revealed the first result of the tragedy, as ambulance workers carried the injured man from the first-aid room to the awaiting ambulance.

It was nearing midnight, the crowd was silent, and the ambulance dashed away with a police car escort.

Then in the early hours, the name of the first dead man was revealed by a harassed-looking N.C.B. spokesman. He was named as Mr. Richard Bannister, a 31 years old development worker, of Coronation Avenue, Grimethorpe.

The spokesman also told reporters that Mr. Ken Upperdine, a 38 years old fitter, of George Street, Low Valley, Wombwell, was in Barnsley Beckett Hospital with facial burns and a fractured femur.

As rescue workers toiled through the night, surfacing only when their oxygen cylinders were exhausted, the extent of the tragedy became more apparent.

Energy Minister and NCB chief visit the pit

MR. TONY BENN, Secretary of State for Energy, was an early visitor to the pit on Friday morning and Sir Derek Ezra, chairman of the N.C.B., arrived about mid-morning.

Yorkshire N.U.M. president, Mr. Arthur Scargill and Mr. Owen Briscoe, secretary, and other union officials told Mr. Benn that they would like a public inquiry into the disaster.

SIR DEREK EZRA

The Energy Minister later paid tribute to the work of the rescue teams and expressed deep sympathy with the deceased's relatives.

Sir Derek and Mr. Scargill also praised the work done by the rescue workers.

Sir Derek said: "I feel extremely distressed that this has happened. Fortunately we haven't been having many of these accidents lately, but it doesn't make them any less tragic when they do occur.

"Every time I hear of a fatality in the industry, it gives me increased determination to reach the year when we shall not have a single fatal accident.

"I believe it is possible because there are many pits that go for years without a fatality, and if they can do it then it can be done throughout the industry."

GRIM-FACED rescue workers wheel a victim from the shaft to the waiting ambulance.

Above and opposite page: The Houghton Main explosion of 1975 as reported in the Barnsley Chronicle.

The phone call that saved a life

Fitter Ken Upperdine (38), made an underground 'phone call at Houghton Main Colliery last Thursday — and that saved his life.

He was on the phone when the explosion ripped through the Newhill seam, killing five of his colleagues.

Ken's father, Mr. Mark Upperdine, Palma Rise, Darfield, a former Darfield councillor, said: "He made the call some distance from the explosion. It blew him off his feet.

"If he had been working, he would have been killed".

Ken, George Street, Low Valley, had returned to work underground on Monday, after sustaining serious injuries in accidents at the pit.

He was off work for four months after he fractured a bone in his head and had a finger amputated in separate accidents.

His father, who worked at Houghton when six men died in a blast in the Melton Field seam 45 years ago, said: "Ken returned to work at Houghton a year, ago. He had worked

THE 5 DEAD

The five men killed in the disaster were:
Mr. Richard Bannister (30), Coronation Avenue, Grimethorpe.
Mr. Irvin Lakin (55), Wath Road, Wombwell.
Mr. Arnold Williamson (59), Norfolk Road, Great Houghton.
Mr. Raymond Copperwheat (42), Norville Crescent, Darfield.
Mr. Leonard Baker, Charles Street, Little Houghton.

A sixth man, Mr. Ken Upperdine, George Street, Low Valley, is in Beckett Hospital, Barnsley, with serious burns and multiple injuries.

Five other men were treated for shock or minor injuries at the colliery. They were: Mr. Fred Woodcock, Mr. Roy Buckley, Mr. W. Arnold, Mr. D. Woodward and Mr. J. Pearson.

as a bus-driver for a time. His wife did not want him to go back, but he is a plucky sort of man."

Ken's son, Christopher, celebrated his 15th birthday on Friday. He has two other children, Tony, who is 14 this month, and Sheryll, who is 16 next month.

Development worker, Mr. Richard Maskell Bannister, said goodbye to his wife, Patricia, and three daughters at 4.30 p.m. on Thursday, and left for the colliery. They never saw him again.

Three hours later he was one of five men killed by the explosion, while working on a split-shift.

Mr. Bannister of Coronation Avenue, Grimethorpe, was born in Ardsley and attended schools in the Barnsley area. He married his wife at St. Joseph's R.C. Church, Kendray, and they moved to Grimethorpe about 11 years ago.

Since leaving school at the age of 15, Mr. Bannister had been employed at Houghton Main Colliery.

His mother-in-law, Mrs. Catherine Bradley of Raymond Avenue, Grimethorpe, said: "Although he lived at Grimethorpe, he maintained he would never leave Houghton Colliery.

"He enjoyed working a split-shift and thought it was the best one", she added.

RICHARD BANNISTER

"He was a very conscientious worker, and you could tell he was worried, because he brought his work problems home".

DOUBLE FUNERAL

Mr. Williamson (59), worked at Houghton for 35 years. He leaves a widow and two daughters, Pamela and Sandra.

The two other men who died, Mr. Leonard Baker, 8 Charles Street, Little Houghton, and Mr. Roy Copperwheat (42), of Norville Crescent, Darfield, were interred at Darfield yesterday (Thursday), after a double funeral service in the parish church.

Mr. Baker, who had worked at the colliery since he was 14, leaves a widow, Connie, who works in the pit canteen, a son, Danny (25), who is a clerk at the pit, and a daughter, Pat (22).

Mr. Lakin was interred at Wombwell cemetery on Wednesday, following a funeral service at Zion Wesleyan Reform Church, George Street, Wombwell.

The funeral service for Mr. Williamson was held at St. Helen's Parish Church, Thurnscoe, yesterday (Thursday) and was followed by interment at Thurnscoe cemetery.

Mr. Bannister will be buried at Ardsley cemetery today (Friday) after a service at St. Luke's Church, Grimethorpe, conducted by Father Eric Cheetham.

KEN UPPERDINE

A keen darts and snooker player, he was a member of Grimethorpe W.M.C. and Miners' Welfare. He was also a motor car fanatic.

BIBLE FOUND

A Bible, which was torn apart by the explosion, was found by a rescue team in the Newhill seam.

It belonged to one of the dead men, 55-years-old Mr. Irvin Lakin, 76 Wath Road, Wombwell, who was secretary of Lundhill Wesleyan Reform Church, whose wife, Dorothy, is a local preacher.

He also leaves two sons, Peter (31), an Environmental Health Inspector, who lives in Barnborough Road, and David (29), who is an Assistant Pastor in Birmingham.

Mr. John Hunt, an official at Lundhill, said: "Mr. Lakin did a tremendous amount of work for the church. His main work concerned young people".

Another victim, Mr. Arnold Williamson, 2 Norfolk Road, Great Houghton, did not like working in the new seam.

His son-in-law, Mr. Graham Howell, a Brierley haulage contractor, said: "He said it was one of the worst places in which he had worked. Water was always coming into the seam.

Chronicle staff covering the tragedy: DON BOOKER, CLEM NEWHAM, JOHN THRELKELD and ALAN WHITEHOUSE.
Photos by STAN BULMER and DON OAKES.

'RUMOURS AND ACCUSATIONS'

The South Yorkshire district coroner, Dr. Herbert Pilling, spoke about rumours and accusations when he opened an inquest on the five victims of the Houghton disaster at Barnsley on Tuesday.

"There have been quite a lot of theories (about the cause of the explosion) bandied about and a lot of rumours," he said.

"Indeed, there have been one or two accusations made publicly. This is very unfortunate in the circumstances, and I think the sooner we can have some sort of answers the better".

Dr. Pilling adjourned the inquest to July 29.

He said that because of difficulties, of which he had been told, it could be 12 months before investigations into the disaster were completed.

But he thought it was totally unreasonable to expect relatives to wait that long for a death certificate and for answers to problems hanging over them.

The coroner said he hoped he would have enough evidence to reach a verdict about the cause of death of the five victims, when he resumed the inquest in six weeks' time.

If there were too many questions unanswered he would have to adjourn it again to such a time as answers were available, but he did not want to have to do this.

He added: "An inquest is a public inquiry and anybody who has anything relative to say can say it. You don't have to wait to be invited.

"It is a duty, never mind a right, to come and say it".

Formal evidence of identification was given by the deceased's relatives and by P.C. Sam Chambers, acting coroner's officer. Dr. Pilling issued burial certificates.

'I don't know how I escaped'

One of the men who survived the explosion, Mr. Ian Lee, a deputy at the colliery for 20 years, led two men, Mr. Fred Woodcock and Mr. Roy Buckley, to safety after the explosion.

The three men heard each other shouting but it was so dusty, as well as very hot and very dry, that they couldn't see each other, and they had to grope their way along the roadway

"When we joined forces I found Fred and Roy were very shocked", said Mr. Lee. "They were almost in a state of panic and I did my best to calm them down a bit.

"Then the air began to clear".

The air continued to get clearer as they made their way to the safety of the pit bottom and Mr. Lee stumbled over his snap bag, which he had lost when the explosion occurred.

When he realised the full extent of the explosion, Mr. Lee said: "I don't know how I escaped injury.

"I wish I hadn't to go down a pit again, but I don't know any other job".

OTHER STATISTICS
YEAR ENDED DECEMBER, 1981

	Saleable Output Tonnes	O.M.S. Face Tonnes	O.M.S. All Workers Tonnes
Barnsley	8,417,108	11.48	2.67
Doncaster	7,179,620	8.04	2.26
North Yorkshire	8,525,168	10.91	2.81
South Yorkshire	7,379,351	9.59	2.24
DIVISION:	31,501,247		

COLLIERY PROFIT AND LOSS ACCOUNTS
(BEFORE CHARGING INTEREST) PER TONNE SALEABLE
12 months ending December, 1981

Barnsley	... ...	£1.34 LOSS
Doncaster	... ...	£2.09 LOSS
North Yorkshire	... ...	£2.32 LOSS
South Yorkshire	... ...	£0.86 LOSS

MANPOWER AS AT DECEMBER ENDING 1981

	Coal Face	Elsewhere U/G	Surface	All Workers
Barnsley	4,081	7,762	2,991	14,834
Doncaster	5,254	7,834	2,665	15,753
North Yorkshire ...	3,820	7,347	3,480	14,647
South Yorkshire ...	4,473	8,030	3,652	16,151
DIVISION	17,628	30,973	12,788	61,385

Above: Yorkshire statistics, 1981. *British Coal*

Right: The expressions on the faces reveal all. Arthur Scargill, Sir Derek Ezra, former chairman of the National Coal Board and Tony Benn, the Energy Minister, at Houghton Main Colliery, the day after the tragedy in which five men died, in 1975.

Photo: British Coal

Below: Arthur Scargill (left) and Lord Mason (third from right), pictured at the unveiling of a memorial to the men who died in the Wharncliffe Woodmoor pit disaster.

Photo: John Marshall

157

Above: Arthur Scargill's last Yorkshire NUM Council meeting, in 1982, before becoming President of the NUM. He is shaking hands with his successor as President of the union's Yorkshire area, Jack Taylor, with branch delegates looking on. Mick Carter (Cortonwood) is pictured far right on the front row. Mr. Carter became a national figure during the 84/85 miners' strike, which was sparked off by the threat to close his pit.

Right: Cortonwood Colliery pictured in 1984.   *Photo: Peter Bradshaw, Stonyford Road, Wombwell.*

The strike

Jackie Keating, a miner's wife, of Dearne Road, Brampton, discovered that the miners' strike of 1984/85 had a profound impact on her. In one respect, the stike challenged accepted beliefs — her attitude towards the police underwent a transformation, their actions causing nightmares. Mining communities, harassed, impoverished and isolated, became societies within a society, governed by their own rules and regulations. In another respect the strike opened up a new world. She wrote "Our Pit, Our Town," a moving, honest appraisal of life in the strike. This is an extract:

"Triona arrived at my home one evening near to Christmas, with Jenny. I was extremely surprised because I hadn't had any contact with Triona since May, and Jenny I hadn't seen much of since my departure from the Action Group. I was quite surprised that Triona had even remembered me let alone gone to the trouble of finding my home. She was very interested in how my own family were coping, and how my parents were. I had spoken of them at length during our last meeting. Fortunately for her, and unfortunately for me, she had caught me at a very upsetting and vulnerable time. Monday of that week had seen some terrible scenes, rioting and violence from both police and miners alike. I had been asked to give first aid to a middle-aged man who had a gaping gash in his leg, showing the bone.

Above: Cortonwood at the beginning of the strike.

Jackie Keating

Below: The start of the big strike: March, 1984. Yorkshire miners' President Jack Taylor (right) and General Secretary, Owen Briscoe, announce that the miners' council have decided to call a strike over the closure of Cortonwood.

Photo: John Marshall

Right and below: Police, mounted and on foot, line-up for a night of confrontation with pickets in Knollbeck Lane, Brampton, near Cortonwood Colliery. The trouble started after a miner went back to work before the end of the strike.

Photographs: Tony Simpson

Above: Arthur Scargill at a rally in Barnsley, probably towards the end of the strike.

173

THE MINER

SPECIAL ISSUE

OF THE NATIONAL UNION OF MINEWORKERS

SATURDAY, JULY 14th, 1984

Whistling in the dark

STOP PRESS Desperate attempts were being made to play down the effects of the miners and dockers strike as *The Miner* went to Press, with much behind the scenes effort to get the dockers to settle. Talks, however, failed on July 13th and seamen's action against privatisation stepped up.

Absurdly constructed news bulletins focussing on obscure foreign stories given great prominence in an attempt to persuade the population at large that all is well. Newspapers abroad, however, carrying detailed stories of deep unrest within Government, fuelling some informed domestic reports that the political knives are already being sharpened. Pound and stock exchange still highly jittery. Despite costly attempts to steady the markets through higher interest rates, confidence still ebbing away.

THE CRACKS ARE SHOWING

The NUM is heading for the greatest industrial victory in the post-war history of Great Britain.

With Government policies in a state of industrial siege — and financial mayhem growing by the day — both Coal Board and Government are on the rack.

Solidarity action and financial support is being stepped up dramatically by members of the public and the unions. People in all walks of life scent that victory is in the air.

The dramatic fall of the pound, which in turn forces higher interest rates and affects inflation, is ripping Government policies apart.

Billions of pounds have been wiped off share values and the squeals of the businessmen are getting louder by the day.

Retreat in the face of the railmen, Liverpool Council, local government elsewhere, remaining GCHQ union members — and total failure to use anti-trade union laws — is destroying Government credibility at a rate of knots.

STRENGTHENED HAND

A massive addition to the Government's problems is the knowledge that the NUM is now more united than at any time since the start of the strike, with the special two-day annual conference in Sheffield *unanimously* passing a sweeping resolution outlining NUM policy and determination to win a resounding victory.

The NUM goes into the next round of talks with the Board on July 18th with its hand immensely strengthened.

The Board itself is already privately admitting that it has lost disastrously, but wants to avoid mentioning this in public so as to save the Government's face.

But the NUM is fully aware of the dirty tricks department and has made it absolutely plain that the closure list must be *withdrawn* and that there will be NO closures on economic grounds.

The NUM position was clearly spelled out at the Edinburgh talks of a week ago and that position was backed wholeheartedly by the National Executive Committee and the Sheffield Conference.

In key-note speeches at the Conference, the national leadership and delegates were in a mood of cast iron determination to notch up the greatest industrial victory ever recorded.

WORLD ADMIRATION

President Arthur Scargill set the tone in his Presidential Address:

"The magnificent courage and determination of our people will see us through to victory," he pledged.

"Over the past 18 weeks I have witnessed among our rank and file a degree of loyalty, commitment and dedication to principle that has roused admiration around the world.

"I have always felt proud and privileged to be a member of this union but never more proud than at the present time."

The President paid particular tribute to the young miners and their wives who had confounded all predictions.

Together they had inspired "a community solidarity the like of which we have never witnessed in any industry or any union ever before."

It was a theme taken up by General Secretary Peter Heathfield in his annual address. All the predictions that mortgages and HP commitments would ensure that young miners would never fight had been shown to be total hogwash.

"They have shown clearly and precisely where their loyalties lies. They have proudly taken up the struggle of their fathers and grandfathers.

"They had endured brutal police intimidation, appalling media attacks and terrible levels of hardship, but had not flinched.

"They had inspired the whole country."

National Vice-President Mick McGahey said this was the greatest strike he had ever been involved in; with a young President leading young members.

"I would hate to be a scab."

The involvement of the young womenfolk was historic and if they had been involved on such a scale in 1926, "we would never have been defeated."

As for the £ crisis, he said that many workers were forced to suffer crisis every day of their lives — "from the womb to the tomb."

MAGNIFICENT RAILMEN

● ASLEF leader Ray Buckton was given a prolonged standing ovation by conference in deep appreciation of the magnificent support of the railmen.

Glowing tributes were paid to the "marvellous men of ASLEF, the NUR, the NUS and the transport workers who were lifting the whole dispute to a resounding victory."

Their support will never be forgotten and would be repaid a thousand times, NUM President Arthur Scargill pledged.

THE KEY RESOLUTION

The key resolution read:

'This extraordinary Annual Conference, meeting in the 18th week of a strike against pit closures and job losses, reaffirms previous Conference decisions to oppose all pit closures other than on grounds of exhaustion, and any reduction in manpower levels; and reaffirms the decisions of the Special Delegate Conference held on 19th April, 1984.

Conference calls for an expanding and developing industry in line with Plan For Coal. The Government must allocate the same financial assistance to our coal industry as is given to nearly all our competitors. At the same time, Britain must begin to build coal-fired power stations, develop combined heat and power programmes, intensify development of the liquefaction project, the gasification scheme, and fluidised bed combustion.

This will ensure an increasing demand for coal, allowing our industry to fulfil the targets projected in

Plan For Coal, and leading towards an annual output of 200 million tonnes as we move into the next century.

Against a background in which the increased use of new technology has combined with a substantial rise in productivity, we demand settlement of the 1983 wages claim. This includes the introduction of the four-day working week, retirement at 55 for all miners on the same terms as those contained in the Redundant Mineworkers' Payment schemes, consolidation of the incentive bonus scheme, implementation of a rate protection scheme (promised in 1981), and all other claims contained in the Union's submission to the Board in 1983.

This Conference places on record its proud acknowledgement of the magnificent achievements of all our members on strike who, together with their families, are providing a lead and an inspiration to the entire British working class.'

COAL NEWS

THE NEWSPAPER OF THE MINING INDUSTRY

No. 283   MARCH 1985   8p

South Yorkshire

As output continues to rise:

HALF OF NUM MEMBERS NOW NOT ON STRIKE....

HALF of all the NUM members in the industry were no longer on strike when Coal News went to press — with record numbers continuing to return to work.

There were 93,000 not on strike — out of the 186,000 total employed by the Board.

On two days alone (February 25 and 26) more men (a total of 5,308) returned to work than during any full five-day week since mid-November. And there were record attendances in all the coalfields.

As more men give up the NUM's strike day by day, the tempo of activity throughout the industry is increasing all the time.

At the beginning of the dispute, deep-mined output was between 400,000 and 500,000 tonnes a week, building up to more than 600,000 tonnes toward the end of 1984. In 1985 it broke through 700,000 tonnes and reached the highest since the dispute started in the week ended February 22 — estimated to be more than 750,000 tonnes (see back page).

First million

Deliveries to customers, which have been running at more than 900,000 tonnes a week, in the same week passed more than one million tonnes for the first time since March 1984. As spring approaches, more coal is on the move than at any time since the dispute began.

The increasing return to work followed rejection by the NUM of proposals presented to them by TUC general secretary Norman Willis for resolving the dispute.

The proposals arose out of discussions with Coal Board chairman Ian MacGregor and deputy chairman James Cowan following the TUC's meeting with Mrs Thatcher and other Ministers at 10 Downing Street.

It was understood that the proposals would, if agreed, be the final agreement covering the central issues of the dispute. They remain available to the NUM.

● **DETAILS — centre**

Around the coalfields

NUM members not on strike on February 26:

North and South Nottinghamshire	96%
South Midlands (excluding Kent with 11.3 per cent)	96%
Western	85%
North Derbyshire	77%
Scotland	44%
North East	47%
Yorkshire	18%
South Wales	6%

Many get tax-free earnings — back page

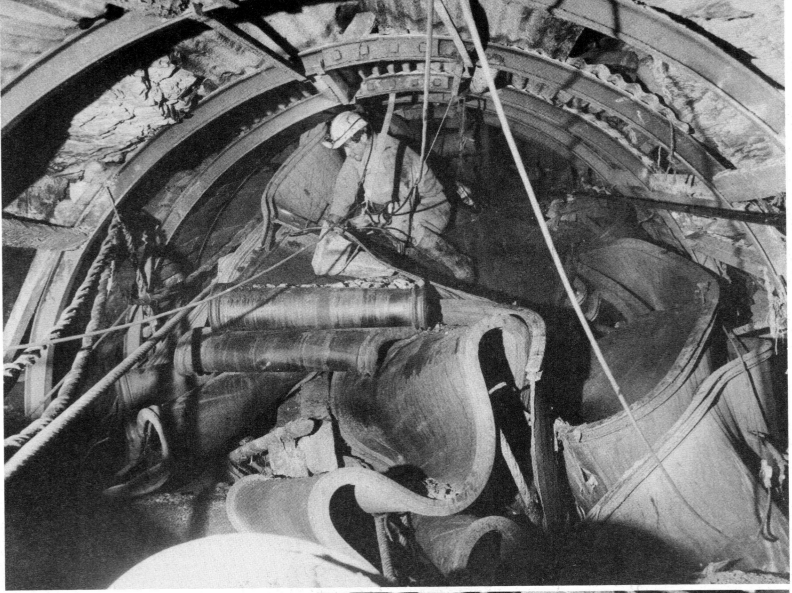

Above: The earth moved during the strike. Without proper underground maintenance nature was left to do its work. Underground damage photographed at North Gawber Colliery.
Right: A mineworker inspecting the hydraulic props at Woolley Colliery.
Photo: British Coal Archives, Mansfield

176

Above: Going . . . going . . . the chimney is demolished at Elsecar Main Colliery in 1985, later to be followed by the rest of the pit.
Photographs: Don Oakes
Left: The old Elsecar branch of the miners' union banner discovered in a box at a Hoyland snooker hall in 1988.

Left: Aeriel photograph of
Rockingham spoil heap.
Photograph: British Coal
Below: Rockingham Colliery site,
1988.

189

Opposite page (top): Grimethorpe Colliery
Photo: Don Oakes

Right: The village of Grimethorpe.
Photo: Don Oakes

Below and opposite page: One of the biggest coal preparation plants in Europe, at Grimethorpe, in the 1980s. Note the size of the parked cars.
Photograph: British Coal

Opposite page: It was not all gloom and doom in the 1980s. Grimethorpe Colliery created a record when they produced five tonnes per manshift in 1988.
Left and below: New pits in the Selby coalfield: Ricall and Stillingfleet.
Photographs: British Coal

Potts. Born at Wombwell Main in 1891, he worked at Wombwell Main and Houghton Main for a spell before emigrating to Canada where he had roughed it on the farms and in the mines. Returning to this country in 1918, he joined the Labour Party and was checkweighman at Wombwell Main. He was the Yorkshire representative on the executive of the Miners' Federation of Great Britain and in 1940 had been appointed Parliamentary Private Secretary to the Minister for Mines. A few weeks after his death Sidney Schofield, a 40 years old Castleford face worker, was adopted Labour candidate, achieving a 28,000 majority in the election. Later Mr. Schofield resigned as MP and concentrated on a career in the NUM, becoming Yorkshire General Secretary. He was succeeded as MP by Mr. Roy Mason, later Lord Mason of Barnsley.

□□□□

The death was announced that year of Mr. George Edward Morris (80), of Kingstone, who had worked in the pits for 62 years, retiring from Barrow Colliery at the age of 75.

□□□□

Barnsley and district had the following pits in 1951: Area No. 4: Frickley, Hemsworth, Monckton No. 1, 2 and 5, Monckton No. 3 and 4, South Elmsall, South Kirkby, Upton, Darfield Main, Dearne Valley, Ferrymoor, Grimethorpe, Houghton Main, Mitchell Main; No. 5: Barrow, Barnsley Main, Monk Bretton, Old Silkstone, Wentworth Silkstone, Silkstone Common, Thorncliffe, Rockingham, Smithywood, Grange, Wombwell Main, Wharncliffe Silkstone; No. 6: North Gawber, Haigh, Wharncliffe Woodmoor 1,2,3, Wharncliffe Woodmoor 4,5, Woolley.

□□□□

Opencast mining, for which the Ministry of Fuel and Power was originally responsible, was taken over by the National Coal Board on April 1, 1952. It had been started as an emergency measure in 1942, and in 1955 produced 11.4 million tons.

□□□□

Speaking at the opening of new pithead baths at Wharncliffe Woodmoor, Carlton, in December, Mr. Hall concentrated on what appeared to be his favourite topic — washing. He said in the old days many miners had resisted the establishment of such baths because they believed coal dust was a good remedy for a cut finger or hand. They also believed water weakened the back. Mr. Hall, referring to the disaster at the mine in the 1930s, said he had returned from Prague when he heard the news, adding: *"I never believed that these pits would come to life again."* After he said that the day would come when garages were erected next to the baths, for miners' cars, Mr. Hall asked: *"Why shouldn't miners come to work in their cars, or even own their homes? This is the way to prevent absenteeism — the miner will work to keep his car or home."* He was disappointed that many young miners were refusing to join the new miners' pension scheme. (On December 29 the Chronicle disclosed that only 40 per cent of mineworkers had enrolled).

□□□□

In the mid 1950s the board operated about 860 pits and there were 500 small mines, the majority with 30 or fewer men underground, which were operated under licence from the board. There were fewer than 12,000 ponies and horses in British mines — the number had fallen from 49,000 in 1930 and 30,000 in 1940.

□□□□

Two assumptions were prevalent in the 50s — that the industry was strike-ridden and that there were more chiefs than Indians. The board disagreed. The Minister of Labour in 1951 said: *"Those who say the coal industry has been just as disturbed by disputes since nationalisation should regard these figures: in the post-war years 1919-1922, working days lost through coal disputes totalled 99 million — in the corresponding post-war years 1945-1948 the figure was nearly three million."* On staff, the Fleck Committee said the criticism was ill informed. *"The proportion of staff — 40,000 out of a total payroll of about three — quarters of a million — is certainly not high. Indeed, we believe that the management of the industry requires a higher proportion."* The proportion of about five per cent of non-industrial employees in the industry compared with about fifteen per cent in industry.

1970s

Jobs: In 1976 21,000 men in the Barnsley borough were employed in mining, representing 27 per cent of total employment and 47 per cent of male employment. The highest concentrations were in the Goldthorpe Employment Exchange area (62 per cent); Royston (58 per cent); Hoyland (57 per cent) and Wombwell (49 per cent). In that year there were fourteen pits and one coking plant in Barnsley and districts, with four pits and two coking plants outside but adjacent to the borough. In 1977/78 the Barnsley coalfield produced more than seven million tonnes of coal, representing twenty five per cent of the Yorkshire coalfield and six per cent of national output.

□□□□

Dereliction: By 1979 mining had left behind 2,145 acres of derelict land including that covered by spoil heaps. In addition, there were 255 acres of disused buildings and spoil heaps awaiting reclamation and 150 acres of coal stocking areas beyond the colliery premises.

□□□□

The impact of surface plant: In the 1970s it was a

feature that the pits were close to the settlements and therefore dominated the image of the settlements: *"Visual intrusion results from the colliery headgear, which towers above the surrounding houses, the open storage of colliery materials and machinery with little or no screening, as well as a jumble of buildings which have grown up haphazardly on the basis of expediency,"* stated a Barnsley council report.

□□□□

Air pollution still caused problems in the 1970s. *"The high pollution levels in parts of the borough are above those regarded as acceptable by the World Health Organisation,"* stated the council's report. *"In these areas it is a combination of dust and pollution from collieries and atmospheric pollution from coking plants and coal-burning domestic premises that are the main contributors to this problem. Whereas the borough council is progressively declaring smoke control areas, almost the whole of the eastern half of the borough would have to be covered by orders for an improvement to be made in real terms."*

□□□□

Mining subsidence: In 1979 Barnsley Borough Council revealed that about 5,000 of the 33,000 council houses had been damaged by subsidence since 1974. If the same ratio applied to private housing — about 48,000 houses — then it was likely that at least 12,000 dwellings had been affected by subsidence between 1974 and 1979. *"This represented 15 per cent of the total housing stock and in its scale is comparable with some great natural disaster or Second World War 'blitz' damage,"* stated the report. The damage ranged from relatively minor cracks in plaster and pathways and jammed doors to major structural damage including severe brickwork fracture, fracture of house drains and tilting of the house block. *"Whilst the National Coal Board pays compensation for damage and replacement or repair of houses destroyed or damaged by subsidence, there is no payment for stress, suffering or inconvenience,"* revealed the report. *"Except for buildings whose owners have negotiated with the NCB for the leaving of a pillar of coal to support them, most buildings in the exposed coalfield are damaged by subsidence from time to time."* In 1978/79, about six miles of railway line were affected by mining activities in the borough. The effect varied from a lowering of the track by a few inches to one case of five feet of settlement. One of the most affected lines was the Sheffield to Leeds line, which had been subjected to a speed restriction of 20 mph. Electricity: Every year in the 70s 5,000 consumers were affected by cuts in the service, caused by subsidence. Water: 153 water mains bursts were reported in 1978. Water courses: At some time, all of the River Dearne, the River Dove as far as Worsbrough and all their tributaries had their flows affected as a result of the rivers being affected by mining. Agriculture: land drainage was often affected, sometimes beyond reasonable restitution.

1980s

Quote by NCB chairman, Ian MacGregor, in the Daily Mirror, dated April 5, 1984, a month after the start of the miners' one year strike: *"It's going to be a long hard haul, a long, hard dispute. These are tough times we live in — and I think they could get even tougher."* He added: *"Eighty per cent of our pits are operating at a profit: a small profit. All we want to do is to make a modest change. We want to close four per cent of the pits that are making heavy losses. I think this is very modest — especially where we guarantee a job to any miner who wants to stay in the industry."* There were 20 threatened pits, with twenty thousand job losses which the NUM claimed were merely the tip of the iceberg — with more job losses to follow. *"Not so,"* replies Mr. MacGregor. *"I am not a butcher"* — that was the phrase Arthur Scargill had tied around him.

□□□□

Quote by James Cameron, journalist and writer, in the middle of the strike, when violence dominated the television screens: *"You can't expect men who have been knocked about for generations to suddenly develop haloes."*

□□□□

Arthur Scargill, President of the NUM, said in January, 1985, when miners were returning to work: *"If the canteen cat walks in twice, the board regard it as two more back at work."*

□□□□

Keith Harper and Patrick Wintour, writing in The Guardian at the end of the strike wrote: *"'Never again' will become the by-word not just within the NUM but in the whole labour movement. However, the impact of the strike on the labour movement, British politics, and the country's shattered sense of nationhood may be in reality a little more complex to digest. The Government may feel that it has won a well-planned victory, akin to Goose Green, but the miners, unlike the Argentinians, cannot be shipped back to their mainland. Instead they will remain a brooding and volatile presence until the next General Election. At the election, the Conservatives will have to show that the strike's scars are not only healing but were necessary."*

□□□□

In 1987, Lord Mason, a former miner, wrote: *"Rapidly increasing poverty in Barnsley over the past five years had a dramatic and depressing impact on the town. I have represented Barnsley for nearly 34 years, and it is unbelievable that such misery could exist on such a large scale as today. I lived through the 1930s and the pre-war depression years, but I never witnessed so many personal pictures of soul destroying unhappiness through being penniless and pleading for help as are evident in Barnsley. This awful and worrying rise in poverty in Barnsley over* the past five years of Tory administration has shattered individuals, families, small communities and our local economy. Crucial poverty indicators, such as the local level of unemployment, the demand of Social Services Section One monies, all reveal a sharp decline in personal and household incomes against a background of increasing job losses, redundancies and pit closures. The scale of poverty is placing intolerable pressures on our local services and resources, both statutory and voluntary, especially in social services, advice services and housing. In Barnsley alone one in five people are unemployed. This is a 19.8 per cent unemployment rate. There has been a 100 per cent increase in the past two years for Welfare Rights Officers referrals (i.e. the number of people calling for advice)."

▢▢▢▢

In July, 1989, British Coal announced profits had doubled to nearly £500 million, with record profits in North Yorkshire (including the former Barnsley coalfield) and South Yorkshire. Nottinghamshire had an operating profit of £73 million. Chairman Sir Robert Haslam said the national output was nearly the same as before the miners' strike, with less than half the workforce and fewer than half the pits and coal faces. In the previous four years 88 pits had either closed or merged. The total workforce, cut from 221,000 to 105,000 at the end of March, 1989, would be down to about 92,000 at the end of August. The North Yorkshire coalfield had turned a £5 million loss in 1988 into a record £18 million operating profit, and achieved the highest productivity rate of any area in the country. The North Yorkshire coalfield workforce stood at 12,500 at the end of the financial year. Sir

Robert said there had been an overall 90 per cent improvement in productivity and colliery costs were down by a third and miners earnings had risen 68 per cent, staying at the top of the earnings league for large industries. But he said the depreciation and high — interest charges meant that the 1988 operating profit was turned into a bottom line loss of £203 million. — The Yorkshire Post.

▢▢▢▢

Extract from The Yorkshire Miner, February 1989: "British Coal's latest wave of closures is now striking home, bringing destruction and disruption to every coalfield in Britain. In Yorkshire, some 4,500 jobs are threatened, as pits in both parts of the coalfield are put into the review procedure or earmarked for closure or drastic cut-backs. South Yorkshire pits were the first to know their fate, with an area review meeting on Tuesday, January 24, and subsequent meetings during the course of that week on the future of individual pits. The greatest shock was the announcement that Barnburgh was to close, with the loss of 680 jobs at the pit and a further 80 at Manvers Main Coking Plant, which now serves that pit alone. More bad news followed at the North Yorkshire review meeting on Friday, February 10, with the old Barnsley area bearing the brunt of the threat to 2,400 jobs. British Coal announced that Royston Drift was to close, with two pit complexes to be put into the review procedure, Houghton/Darfield and the West Side complex, including Denby Grange, Park Mill, Calder and the Woolley washery."

Later the Darfield unit closed but Houghton survived, together with part of the West Side complex.

Lord Mason

Chapter 12
Mining memories

Jack Lawson

Jack Lawson was an ex-miner, a writer and an M.P. He was born in 1881, educated at Board School and was elected for the Chester-le-Street Parliamentary division of Durham in 1919 (in the 1945 Labour Government he was Secretary of State for War). In the 1930s he wrote a number of popular novels set in mining towns, including "Under the Wheels". Like A. J. Cronin, author of "The Stars Look Down," Lawson adopted a fresh approach to miners and their towns, portraying them in warm terms, in sharp contrast to most writers at that time. I have used extracts from "Under the Wheels" to illustrate what life was like in a coalfield in 1909.

"Westburn is not much of a 'place' to look at. A dozen long streets. All the houses have steep roofs falling just over the doorway and suggestive of attics. Sanitary conveniences are over the road. You must cross the road in sight of all. The fronts of the houses are relieved by gardens. These sombre-looking streets with their houses into which you see plainly as you pass — houses only screened from each other by a rough, low, wooden partition — these streets overlooked by pit-gear and engine houses would repel the stranger. But the fact remains that Westburn is honeycombed with sentiment, a rich, fragrant sentiment that colours the colourless, throws lustre over the dull. The stranger sees the shell of things, but the initiated knows throbbing and moving things beyond the power of eyes. They see homes, sons, daughters, mothers, fathers, relations and friends — rooted, intertwined. The tag that 'Art is long and life is short' may run well, and the man who made it may prefer art, but the people of Westburn wouldn't understand that kind of genius.

"A colliery it may be, but it is also a village. Families have been long-rooted, and inter-marriage has connected each home so that human strands have been knitted together until the village is one whole. There everybody knows everyone else and they know their business, too. As comfortable-looking Mrs. Jones said, one day in the store: 'It was their business to know each other's business, for they were all kin, and folks must talk about summat.'"

The home: "Wide was the place where the great fire burned. You could have lost a scuttle full on the fire. Black and shiny was everything about it. Hard-driving patient hands had black-lacquered and black-leaded its respective parts — oven, too — so often that its daily brush up kept it fresh from one weekend to another. Every Friday it got its new, shiny, black dress, but the dress being brushed daily, it looked always new. The mantelpiece, with its coloured vases, was high and under it ran a long, bright, brass rod. There was a spacious 'plainness to comfort' about the place."

The disaster: "Rumours of a thing so grim that it was told in whispers. Slowly it spread through Westburn, but none spoke it aloud. A pit had fired. There was no wireless in those days; evening newspapers came late, and pits were remote. But the news spread in Westburn as it was doing in every colliery in the north, until it was spoken aloud with sad certainty. That afternoon a devastating pit explosion had occurred.

"West Stanley was a quiet village on that Tuesday afternoon in February 1909. It was almost four o'clock. Men and boys would soon pour out of the pit. Dinners were in the oven, or in pans on the fire, where they had been roasting and boiling until they were ready for the hungry black ones. An ordinary working day, working to its end, when the regular ring of heavy boots would be heard coming down the streets telling the end of the shift. Just an ordinary day. Like the boom of a far-off heavy gun it came. Men close by the colliery saw a great volume of smoke rise from the shaft. A lesser boom and terrifying tongues of flame leapt high. Around the shaft itself men heard a far-off sound, increasing to a roar, and as they looked a large ball of fire leaped from the pit mouth, followed by a thick cloud of dust. They were knocked down, plunged into darkness, and again standing in clear air all in a moment.

Above: Cleaning the Yorkshire Range, the dirtiest job in the home.
Photo: Yorkshire Art Circus/ Jack Hulme.

"Those who saw it knew that nothing was left alive in the track of that flaming holocaust. In the flicker of an eyelid men and boys had been turned into cinders. Dinners were forgotten, houses emptied, doors left open; clatter of feet and cries of running women.

"Men did not know how many had been saved — if any. Blacker than the night gathering around them grew the hopelessness within, which only crowds knew . . .

"They were but a symbol of those endless crowds that have stood under the pulleys for two centuries in this land, dumbly watching the wheels turned to bring to the surface the empty shell of those they thought to have welcomed and served. They were not the first, nor the last to know the meaning of those terrible words: 'The pit has fired.' And the totalling of the victims would make a nation."

Charlie Bennett

A letter from Charlie Bennett, Middlestown, Wakefield, in *The Yorkshire Miner* newspaper in August 1987. *"I started work at Woolley Colliery in 1928. At that time, men going into the workings would strip off most of their clothing at the pony stables, about 200 yards from the shaft bottom, because of the heat. Some men would travel more than half an hour before reaching their workplace.*

"Your older readers will know all about tramming. For a period, I was a 'market trammer', which meant you were sent to tram for any collier whose trammer had not turned up. At that time wages were paid "aht o't cap.' A market trammer might have to find five different colliers for his money, and most colliers would try to pay market trammers less than he should. Many fist fights developed in the pit yard on Fridays.

"Any man who might have proven troublesome to the management would find himself blacklisted and, because the same owners owned most of the pits in the area, a man blacklisted would not be set on at any of the pits. Victimisation gave the union plenty to do. Pits in those days, under the old contract system, were a jungle. Men were conditioned to behave like beasts, to develop teeth and claws.

"One can only hope that Britain's miners of today, as well as the British people, will not allow privatisation to return to the coalfields."

Arthur Brant

Lady luck deserted Arthur Brant when he was killed in the explosion at North Gawber Colliery in 1935.

He had always regarded himself as lucky. He had served in the First World War, had been gassed several times and had been badly injured when a shell exploded near him. Yet he had survived the war.

His widow, from Four Lane Ends, Mapplewell, who identified his body after the pit explosion, said she could hardly recognise the body because his face had been nearly burned away. Earlier a neighbour had told Mrs. Brant she had seen her husband on a stretcher on his way to hospital and it looked as if he had survived the disaster. But it transpired that the man on the stretcher was Mrs. Brant's son, William, a deputy at North Gawber.

A reporter with the *Yorkshire Evening News* wrote: *"The warmth of the September sun brought no comfort to the homes where husbands and sons were missing, their burnt and battered bodies lying in the improvised mortuary at the colliery. I toured the homes today and, as I talked to weeping women and their wide-eyed children, I realised the stark horror of the disaster. They told me of fearful visits to the mortuary, where they were called upon to identify their men, and spoke of the terrible burns and other disfigurements."*

A survivor told the reporter: *"All at once there was a gap in the atmosphere underground. Then it seemed that some giant breath was dragging me forward with tremendous suction.*

"Just as I was falling there was a terrific flash and I was flung against the coal face. Eventually I was pulled away before the fire reached me."

(Nineteen mineworkers were killed in the explosion).

Charles Page

Eleanor Bayley

Mrs. Eleanor Bayley, of Macclesfield, was 19 years old and a nurse when she witnessed the sight of 57 white shirts and coffins lined up for the victims of the Wharncliffe Woodmoor explosion in 1936. *"I was between training courses in nursing and had been asked to help out with relief duties for the District Nurse — that is how I became involved in the rescue operations."*

Eleanor, (nee Caswell) was roused from bed at 4 a.m. by her father, a member of the pit rescue team, with the words: *"Cum on lass, there has been an accident at the pit."* It was 6.30 a.m. when the first man was brought out. He died a few hours later. *"We saw rescue workers going in with canaries and bringing them out dead so we expected the worst."*

The bodies were brought out, washed and then laid on straw for identification.

"We had to get down on our knees and armed with buckets of water we washed the grimy, burned and disfigured bodies — it was a pitiful sight that will never leave my memory."

Eleanor was working alongside the midwife, Mrs. Bateman. *"We came across her brother-in-law but didn't realise it was him until we had washed the dirt away. Then came the body of my Sunday school teacher and lads that I had gone to school with. Last messages to wives, mothers and sweethearts, and*

hidden in their pit clogs, were handed to the authorities."

Charles Page

Charles Page (83) Stonyford Road, Wombwell, started work at Darfield Main Colliery in 1918 and his first job involved putting metal discs (motties) on nine inch nails.

The discs were collected by miners before they went underground and then the discs were put on the tubs so that office staff could identify the miners who had filled them when the coal arrived on the surface.

When the pit ran out of discs, miners used chalk to put a number on their tubs.

Mr. Page remained in the office for a month and then the pit bought its first Ford-T truck to replace the horse and cart used to deliver miners' home coal.

"I got the job as a driver's mate. The driver was Irving Camplejohn, whose family later ran a bus company, and we delivered coal to miners' homes. We also delivered loads to the owners of the pit, the Mitchell family, who lived at Wath and at Upperwood Hall, Darfield. All the coal had to be hand picked for the Mitchell family. I worked on the lorry for nine months and then went underground."

He remembers receiving what was known as the Sankey Money (named after Lord Sankey who awarded the miners a big wage bonus at the end of the First World War). *"I was just over 14 and I thought I had received a windfall. The one-off payment was probably a £1, more than my weekly wage."*

Newcomers were not supposed to take a pony down the pit, the rules stating that they had to be accompanied by an experienced lad. But Mr. Page was tall for his age and management allowed him to take charge of a pony on the first day. *"My pony was called Tigser; he was so intelligent he could do the job without help from humans. Management thought a lot about ponies. When there was a big roof fall one day, the manager asked: 'Are the ponies all right?' Ponies cost money but we get men for nothing."*

Pensions were small in the 1920s and 1930s and men worked until they dropped. Just before he left Darfield Main, to work at Upton Colliery in 1929, there was still a 70 year old man called Finch working on the coal face. *"I remember talking to miners in their late 60s and telling them that one day we would get holidays with pay. The didn't believe a word. But we got three days with pay in 1938 and a week with pay in 1940.*

"In those days, old miners were always punctual. When we were children, we knew what time it was when we saw the men, many with walking sticks, making their way from Low Valley to Houghton Main Colliery."

Colin Moore

Colin Moore didn't know all the names of the miners at Darfield Main Colliery — but he knew their

212

faces and their lamp numbers. For more than 40 years he worked in the lamp room at the pit, starting in 1936 and retiring as the man in charge in the early 1980s.

"I once arranged to see one of our mineworkers who lived in Lundwood and I was half way there before I realised I didn't know his surname; just his number, 992," said Mr. Moore, aged 68, of Wainwright Place, Wombwell. "When I arrived at Lundwood, I had to find someone who knew everyone at Lundwood and then describe my colleague to him, so I could track him down.

"I can still link the lamp numbers with the men. For instance, Edwin Wainwright who worked at the pit and who later became an M.P., had number 25."

Mr. Moore had 1,500 lamps to look after and it was his job to make sure they were in good repair and ensure each lamp was handed to the correct miner before he went underground.

"When a miner was killed or seriously injured the accident affected us. His lamp on the rack in our room was a constant reminder of the accident. The sadness affected the entire pit. Darfield Main, known as the Valley, was a good pit; it had a friendly atmosphere about it."

His first boss was Johnny Froggatt from Darfield. "I remember him wielding his wooden mallet, trying to loosen a lamp which had become damaged and which would not unscrew. Johnny missed his lamp and struck his leg a mightly blow and he didn't flinch. I thought this man was exceptional; then I realised he had a wooden leg. When the straps broke on his artificial leg, I had to go to his home to collect his spare one . . . it must have been quite a sight

Left: 'Motties' — the discs placed on coal tubs. _F. Burgin_

Below: Darfield Main Colliery, the home of the human nightingale.

firmness, fairness and good communications are required. There were men who did not need supervision, practical pit men who only required to know what you wanted. Then you let them get on with the job. These men were the salt of the earth and without them few pits would work successfully. At the other end of the scale you had the awkward squads, men who were hell bent on forcing their will on others, very often to the detriment of the other men. You had to deal with them with firmness and without compromise.

"Man management techniques varied from pit to pit, depending on the size of the catchment area. The larger the catchment area the more difficult and militant the men appeared to be, probably because there were so many divided opinions among them. On the other hand, the small catchment areas produced the family pit, where the men were drawn from nearby villages and many of them were closely related. Industrial relations problems were rare at these pits. There were exceptions. Wentworth Silkstone, with its pine forest, was a family pit with good men, although most of them came from Dodworth. Yet the Dodworth pit was very militant. Before I arrived at Wentworth, the pit had a poor safety record but we got the men safety motivated and we twice reached the national finals of the NCB

competitions, at Drury Lane and at the Opera House, Blackpool. We had our own pit newspaper with stories from the safety officer, and even horse racing and gardening tips supplied by Gordon Totty of Dodworth." When the colliery closed in the late 70s, the NCB, out of respect to the men, transferred them to Houghton Main Colliery, where part of the Dunsil seam was earmarked for the men. This kept them together as a team. Some men were nervous about the transfer: they had always worked in a drift mine and the thought of descending a shaft frightened them.

Mr. Hunt went on to be a manager in the management team which rebuilt the Barnsley coalfield, working on the Grimethorpe drift as well as the shaft deepening at pits which were linked underground to Grimethorpe, retiring in 1981. He came up the hard way — valuable experience when dealing with miners. "You are either a pit man or not. That goes a long way towards getting the men's respect. Respect is very important. You may not be at the top of the popularity polls but then popularity is the cheapest commodity you can buy. The years have brought affluence and a tragedy. Today we have a selfish society, a society that has lost that old camaraderie which has been replaced with greed and envy and a disregard for others or their property."

Below: The southside drift at Grimethorpe, part of Barnsley coalfield's reconstruction programme, on which Mr. John Hunt worked. *Photo: British Coal.*

NCB SOUTHSIDE DRIFT 1980

Frank Leake

Mr. Frank Leake wrote the following letter to Coal News in 1987: *"The 40th anniversary of nationalisation of the coal industry featured in Coal News brings back memories. My father spent almost 50 years in the pits and I, like many other sons of miners, were accustomed only to mining life. Whilst the Arley Colliery Company (Warwickshire) was a good one, as mining goes, you felt they had influence on you not only at work but at home and at leisure as well. You lived in their house, used their water and depended on their electricity. I was pleased to see on January 1, 1947, the sign over the Time Office at Arley stating that this colliery was now under the management of the NCB; I went underground that day with the impression of a new and better future.*

"The year before vesting day was critical. A fuel shortage occupied the minds of the Government and industry and efforts were being made to produce considerably more than the 180 million tonnes forecast in 1946. Incidents that year included Arthur Horner being elected NUM Secretary in place of Ebby Edwards; Hugh Gaitskell becoming Parliamentary Secretary to the Ministry of Fuel and Power, with Manny Shinwell as the Minister; the Football League and Association putting an embargo on midweek cup ties because of absenteeism in mining and other industries; the Government turning down a request for a two week holiday for mining; mineworkers being warned not to leave their work to take seasonal work in agriculture and the TUC urging all trade unionists to save coal. In addition, a plan was drawn up to close certain industries if the coal position deteriorated in the winter.

"Mr. Shinwell said there were ten electric battery and 43 diesel powered locos in use underground. Of the 229 collieries employing more than 1,000 men, 173 had pithead baths. There were 23,191 ponies underground. Mr. J. Craddock, a Northumberland filler, created a new record by filling 73 tubs (37 tons), in seven and a half hours.

"A tremendous difference exists 40 years later. Successive governments have had different ideas about the industry's size, but all have realised the importance of an efficient base for energy requirements. The only rationing is dictated by price, and the request for two weeks' holiday seems far distant compared with the present entitlement. Pit ponies are no longer with us and Mr. Craddock's record has been overtaken by mechanisation."

Below: Back street social rituals insisted that the men don aprons to serve sandwiches and cups of tea to the wives and children at special street functions. The giant teapot (see picture) was indispensable, as it was at chapel parties.
Photo: Yorkshire Arts Circus/ Jack Hulme.

Chapter 13
Scrapbook

Some photographs arrived too late to be included in the earlier chapters and therefore have been put in the scrapbook. They deal with all kinds of subjects, from the bizarre — like the men testing early rescue equipment — to the official opening of a miners' welfare, demolished nearly 30 years ago; from the pages of The Barnsley Chronicle, circa 1939, to nostalgic street scenes in Barnsley.

Miners going down the Shaft of Coal Mine.

Far left: A distinguished group of men outside an unknown Barnsley pit. *F. Burgin.*

Left: An American postcard depicting miners in the 1900s. *F. Burgin.*

Opposite page: Sinking a mine shaft at the turn of the century.
Yorkshire Mining Museum/Leeds City Museum.

Left: The Eldon works of Reynolds and Wadsworth at the bottom of The Arcade. (*See Filling the Gaps, page 200*).

Below and over page: The following street scenes show a mining town at the peak of its influence and power: Barnsley in the 1900s. In Peel Square you can see M. Lowrance and Son (*see Growth of the Pits, page 13*). Also pictured are Cheapside and Queen Street.
F. Burgin.

BARNSLEY. PEEL SQUARE. 10.

QUEEN STREET, BARNSLEY.

663 QUEEN ST. BARNSLEY.

The former Rockingham Colliery
site, pictured near Shortwood,
Hoyland, in 1988, before opencast
operations began.

Colin Fletcher.

Acknowledgements

My thanks to: Ruth Vyse and her staff at Barnsley Library, Mr. Gordon Jones at Mitchell and Darfield Welfare Institute, Mr. Alan Billingham, Mr. Alan Stevenson, Mr. Gordon Crossland, Mr. P. Thompson (Yorkshire NUM), Mr. Mike Thomas, Mr. Dennis Towle (British Coal), Mr. Arthur Evans, Mr. Albert Riley, Mr. Cliff Mayes, Mr. Peter Taylor, Mrs. June Walton, Mrs. Kath Parkin, Mrs. J. Keating, the staff at the Yorkshire Mining Museum at Caphouse Colliery, Mr. Ian Thompson, Ms Hazel Whitworth, Debbie Gough, Mr. Ian Harley, Mr. Roy Sabine, Mr. John Marshall, Mrs. S. Cope, Mrs. M. Crossland and to all who have contributed photographs.

Bibliography

The Clarkes of Silkstone, R.A. Roberts
Aristocratic Enterprise, Graham Mee
Labouring Barnsley, 1816-56, F.J. Kaijage
Diary of Joseph T. Knowles, 1886.

Martyrdom of the Mine (1898), Edward A. Rymer.
Explosions in Coal Mines: the tragedy of the Oaks Colliery, Brian Elliott.

Index

Page numbers in italics denotes photograph or illustration.